Esse… Skills for Reading Success:

Strategies for Reading Comprehension and Test Taking

by Howard I. Berrent, Ph.D.
and Edward R. Nasello

RALLY! EDUCATION, LLC
Glen Head, New York

ISBN 1-58380-990-2

Published 2005
Printed in the U.S.A.

Cover Designer: Jean-Paul Vest
Book Designer: Lori Harley
Editor: Pat Keiserman
Illustrator, pages 92 and 93: Donna Stackhouse

RALLY! **EDUCATION**
22 Railroad Avenue
Glen Head, NY 11545
tel 888·99·RALLY
fax 516·671·7900
www.RALLYEDUCATION.com

Essential Skills for Reading Success

Strategies for Reading Comprehension and Test Taking

Table of Contents

Introduction page 4

PART A: The 14 Essential Skills for Reading Success—*One-by-One* page 5

Skill 1: Facts and Details page 6
Skill 2: Main Idea page 11
Skill 3: Sequence page 16
Skill 4: Language and Vocabulary page 21
Skill 5: Character, Plot, and Setting page 25
Skill 6: Cause and Effect page 30
Skill 7: Compare and Contrast page 35
Skill 8: Facts and Opinions page 40
Skill 9: Predict Outcomes page 45
Skill 10: Reach Conclusions page 50
Skill 11: Make Inferences page 55
Skill 12: Point of View and Purpose page 60
Skill 13: Literary Forms and Sources of Information page 65
Skill 14: Prior Knowledge page 70

PART B: The 14 Essential Skills for Reading Success—*All Together* page 75

Section 1: Modeled Instruction and Guided Instruction **page 76**

Section 2: Independent Study **page 85**

Theme: *Up, Up, and Away*
Selection 1: *Hot Air Balloons* page 86
Selection 2: *To the Top* page 92
Selection 3: *Way, Way Up* page 98
Selection 4: *Our Sky* page 104

Introduction

Welcome to ***Essential Skills for Reading Success:*** *Strategies for Reading Comprehension and Test Taking.* Being a successful reader means that you understand what you read. There are fourteen important skills you need to be a great reader. This book teaches you strategies, which are ways to use the skills when you read. It also teaches you how to answer reading comprehension questions on tests.

Essential Skills for Reading Success has different kinds of reading selections and different types of questions. You will read passages that are poems, and other passages that give you information, tell a story, or explain how to do something. You will be asked multiple-choice questions and questions that require you to write out an answer. When you finish this book you will be a better reader and a better test taker.

Essential Skills for Reading Success is made up of two parts:

Part A will teach you the essential reading comprehension skills one-by-one.

Part B will teach you the essential reading comprehension skills all together.

Throughout the book, we will provide *Strategies, Hints,* and *Reminders* to make learning easier for you. First we will model what we teach. Then we will guide you. Finally we will provide you with independent study to try on your own what you have learned.

When you finish ***Essential Skills for Reading Success*** you will be a better reader and a better test taker.

PART A

The 14 Essential Skills for Reading Success

One-by-One

Each of the fourteen reading comprehension skills are taught one-by-one in this part. First you will read a passage. You will then be asked some questions.

In **Modeled Instruction**, we will teach you a strategy that you can use to answer each question. Then we will explain each of the answer choices. We will show you why some of the choices are not correct. We will explain why the correct choice is the answer.

In **Guided Instruction**, we will provide *Hints* for you on how to answer the question. The first question will be multiple-choice. The second question will ask you to write out the answer.

In **Independent Study**, you will be on your own. You will answer multiple-choice and open-ended questions.

1 Facts and Details
2 Main Idea
3 Sequence
4 Language and Vocabulary
5 Character, Plot, and Setting
6 Cause and Effect
7 Compare and Contrast
8 Facts and Opinions
9 Predict Outcomes
10 Reach Conclusions
11 Make Inferences
12 Point of View and Purpose
13 Literary Forms and Sources of Information
14 Prior Knowledge

Skill 1: Facts and Details

This is the information that is in the passage. Every passage has many facts and details.

Directions: Read the passage below. The passage is followed by questions that can be answered by finding facts and details in the passage. Use this passage to answer all the questions on pages 8–10.

Apple Picking

1 Tom is going to pick apples. He and his mom pick apples every year. They go to the same place. It is called the Apple Barrel. Tom loves to pick apples there. He picks only big, red apples.

2 "We are almost there," says his mother.

3 "How many apples will we pick?" Tom asks.

4 "We will fill one basket. We will not eat more than that!"

5 Tom laughs. He thinks about what they will do with the apples. Tom likes to eat them right out of the basket. He also likes apple pie. And he likes baked apples. They are hot and so good to eat! Applesauce is good, too.

6 "I can't wait to bite an apple," says Tom. "My mouth is ready right now!"

7 Tom's mother laughs. She parks the car. They get out. A man gives them a basket. He hands Tom an apple picker. The picker will help Tom reach the apples that are up high.

8 Tom runs ahead. He looks for the best tree. It will have many big, red apples on it. He keeps looking. Then he finds it.

9 He picks some of the apples from the tree. The picker can reach up high. It helps Tom pick apples that are up high.

10 "Good job, Tom," says his mother. "You are very good at picking apples."

11 Then she says, "Our basket is full now."

12 "One more!" says Tom. He raises the picker. He puts it over an apple. He pulls gently. The apple drops in the basket. Tom lowers the basket.

13 "This one is for you!" Tom tells his mother.

14 "Thank you, Tom!" says his mother. "Now let's go home and make a pie!"

Modeled Instruction

Directions: You can answer this question by finding facts and details in the story. Use the strategy to help you find the answer.

1 Tom loves—

Ⓐ to go to school

Ⓑ to pick apples

Ⓒ to go to the store

Ⓓ to ride his bike

Strategy: Look at the key words in the question. Find those words in the story. Read that part of the story. This will help you know what the answer is. The key words for this question are "Tom loves."

Use this strategy to decide which answer is correct.

Ⓐ to go to school

Tom might love to go to school. But this story does not tell you about school. So, *choice "A" cannot be correct.*

Ⓑ to pick apples

The key words "Tom loves" and the words "to pick apples" are in the first paragraph. The story tells you that Tom loves to pick apples. So, *choice "B" must be the correct answer.*

Ⓒ to go to the store

There are no details in the story about going to a store. So, *choice "C" cannot be correct.*

Ⓓ to ride his bike

Tom might love to ride his bike. But the story does not tell you that. So, *choice "D" cannot be correct.*

Guided Instruction

Directions: Use the hints to answer the questions below. For question 2, you must choose the correct answer. For question 3, you will need to write out your answer.

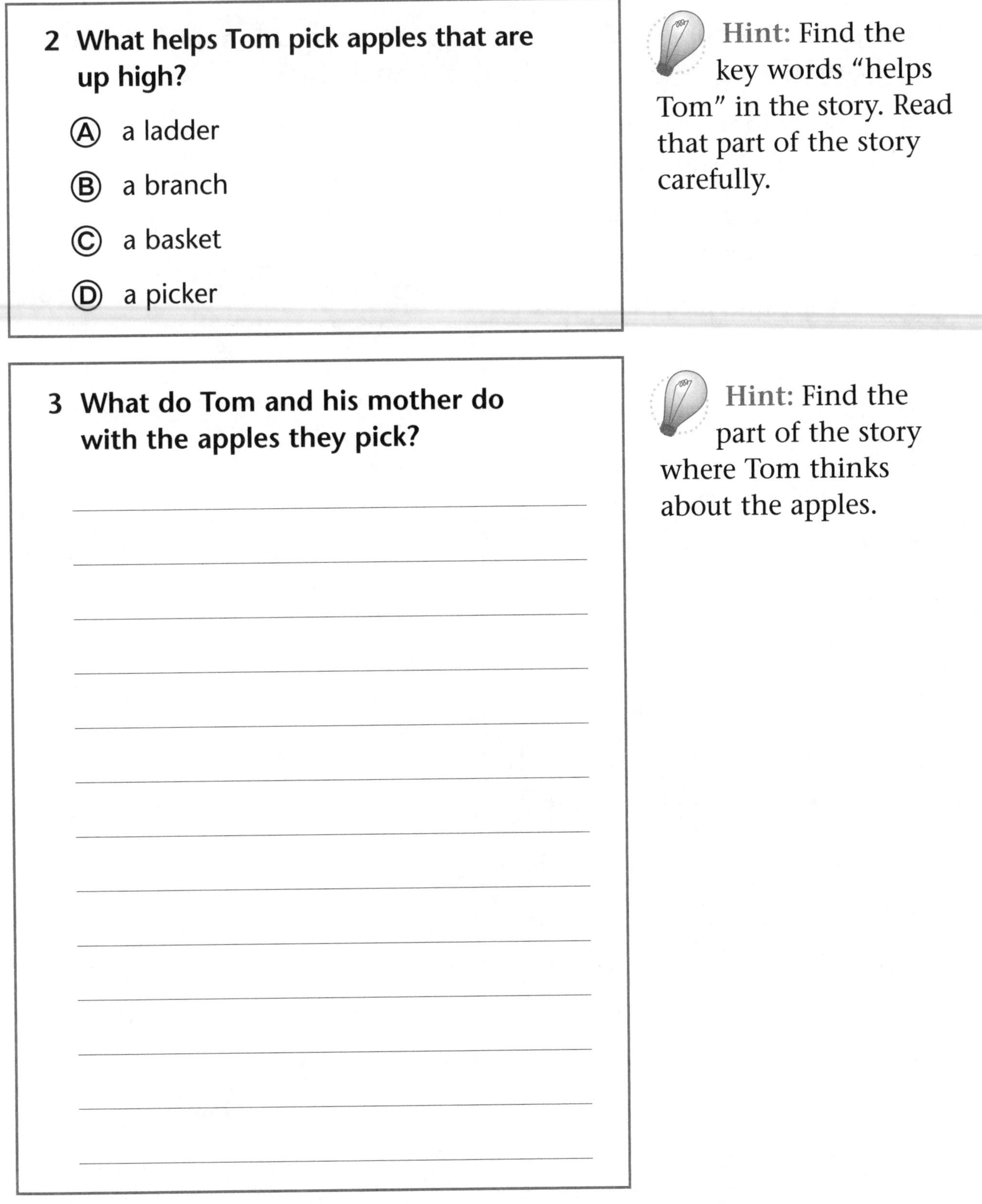

2 What helps Tom pick apples that are up high?

Ⓐ a ladder

Ⓑ a branch

Ⓒ a basket

Ⓓ a picker

Hint: Find the key words "helps Tom" in the story. Read that part of the story carefully.

3 What do Tom and his mother do with the apples they pick?

Hint: Find the part of the story where Tom thinks about the apples.

Independent Study

Directions: Answer the following questions on your own. For questions 4, 5, and 6, choose the correct answer. For question 7, you must write out your answer.

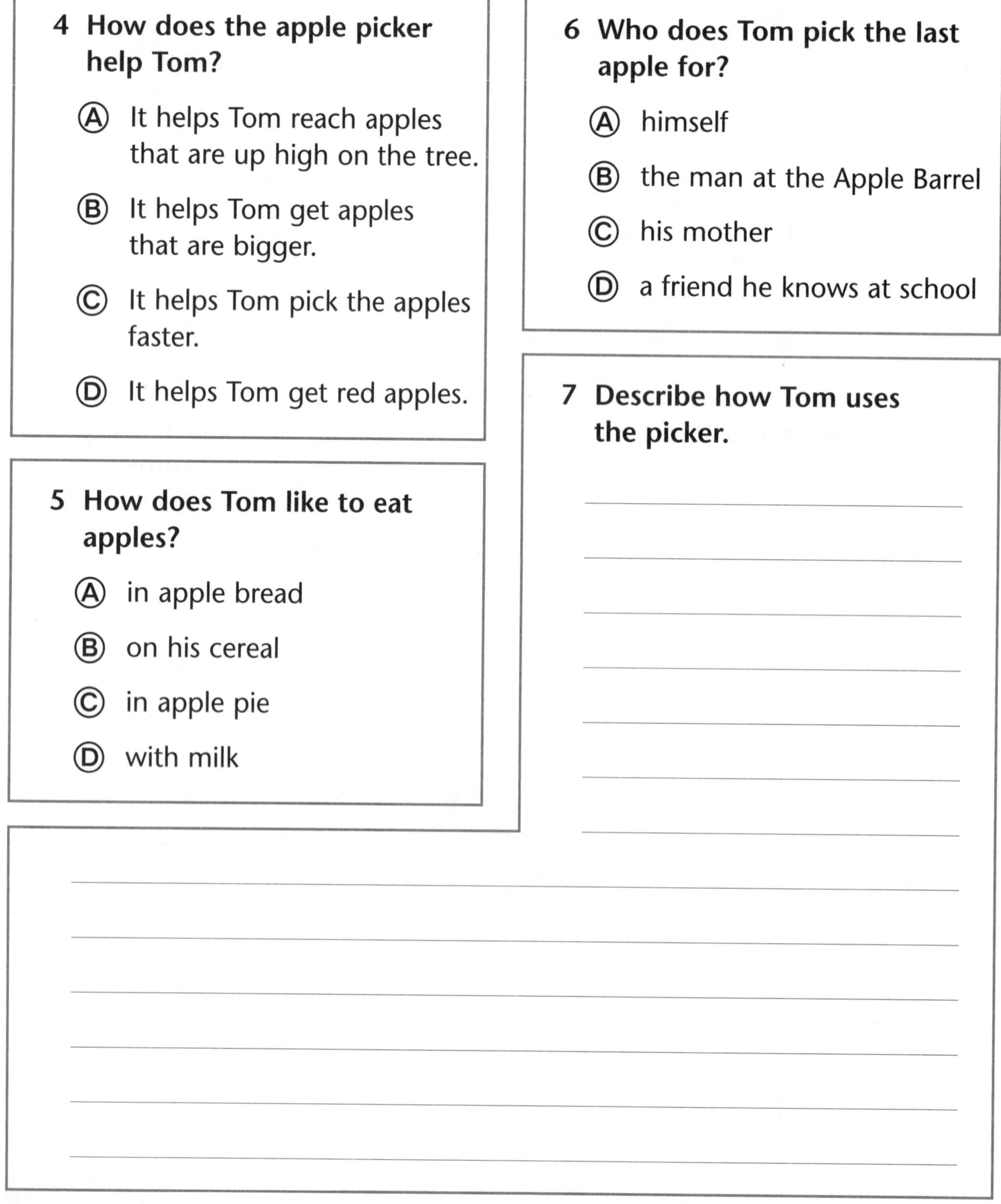

4 How does the apple picker help Tom?

Ⓐ It helps Tom reach apples that are up high on the tree.

Ⓑ It helps Tom get apples that are bigger.

Ⓒ It helps Tom pick the apples faster.

Ⓓ It helps Tom get red apples.

5 How does Tom like to eat apples?

Ⓐ in apple bread

Ⓑ on his cereal

Ⓒ in apple pie

Ⓓ with milk

6 Who does Tom pick the last apple for?

Ⓐ himself

Ⓑ the man at the Apple Barrel

Ⓒ his mother

Ⓓ a friend he knows at school

7 Describe how Tom uses the picker.

Skill 2: Main Idea

The main idea is what the whole passage is about. A passage may be about more than one thing. The main idea is what it is mostly about. The main idea of a paragraph or sentence is what that paragraph or sentence is mostly about.

Directions: Read this passage. The questions after the passage ask about main ideas. Use the passage to answer all the questions on pages 13–15.

1 Did you ever see a squirrel bury a nut? How does the squirrel find it later? Squirrels love nuts. They break the nut open. They take it out of its shell. They lick the nut. And they rub it. Then they bury it. Why does the squirrel do all this to the nut? It leaves a smell on the nut. This smell helps the squirrel find the nut later. It can even find the nut under snow!

2 A squirrel is busy all the time. It gathers food. It stores the food in many places. The food is for winter. And the squirrel works on its nest.

3 A squirrel builds its nest in a tree. The nest is up high. The squirrel uses twigs and leaves. The nest is like a big ball. It is soft inside. The squirrel puts in fur, feathers, and bark. This is where the squirrel stays warm in winter. This is where baby squirrels are born.

4 A squirrel can have four to six babies. They stay in the nest for ten weeks. Then they come out. They learn to look for food. They learn how to store it. They learn how to build a nest. Then they go out on their own.

Squirrel. Photographer: Joe Martin.
Courtesy of the U.S. Fish and Wildlife Service.

Photographers: John and Karen Hollingsworth. Courtesy of the U.S. Fish and Wildlife Service.

5 A squirrel has sharp teeth. It uses them to break open nuts. The squirrel has to keep its teeth sharp. For an hour or so every day, the squirrel chews on branches. This keeps its teeth sharp.

6 We see a lot of gray squirrels. We see red ones, too. They are quite a bit alike. But they are different, too. They are different colors. Also, a gray squirrel is a little bigger. The gray squirrel has a long bushy tail. The red squirrel's tail is not as long and bushy.

7 Squirrels have been around for a long time. Squirrels are quite smart. They know how to stay alive. They save food for winter. And they are always looking for food. Have you seen a squirrel on a bird feeder? They love the seeds. And they always get in!

Modeled Instruction

Directions: You can answer this question by finding the main idea of the passage. Read each answer. Use the strategy to find the right answer.

1 What would be the best title for this passage?

Ⓐ "Small Animals"

Ⓑ "Animal Nests"

Ⓒ "Squirrel Babies"

Ⓓ "Busy Squirrels"

Strategy: A good title tells the main idea of a passage. Think about all the information you read in the passage. Ask yourself, "What is the passage **mostly** about?" Then decide what the main idea is.

Use this strategy to decide which answer is correct.

Ⓐ "Small Animals"

A squirrel is a small animal. But this passage tells only about squirrels. It does not tell about other small animals. So *choice "A" cannot be correct.*

think

Ⓑ "Animal Nests"

Paragraph 3 tells how a squirrel builds its nest. But the passage does not tell about other animal nests. It only tells about squirrel nests. So *choice "B" cannot correct.*

Ⓒ "Squirrel Babies"

Paragraph 4 tells about squirrel babies. None of the other paragraphs tell about squirrel babies. The whole passage is not mostly about squirrel babies, so *choice "C" cannot be correct.*

Ⓓ "Busy Squirrels"

Every paragraph in the passage tells about squirrels and all the things they do. In paragraph 2, it says that a squirrel is busy all the time. So, *choice "D" must be the correct answer.*

Guided Instruction

Directions: Use the hints to answer the questions below. For question 2, you must choose the correct answer. For question 3, you will need to write out your answer.

2 Paragraph 3 in the passage tells mostly about—

Ⓐ tall trees

Ⓑ red squirrels

Ⓒ squirrel nests

Ⓓ leaves and twigs

Hint: To answer this question you only need to look at paragraph 3. Think about what important facts can be found in this paragraph. Ask yourself what most of these facts are about.

3 What is paragraph 4 mainly about? Remember to list facts and details that tell what the main idea is.

____

____

____

____

____

____

____

____

____

____

____

____

Hint: Think about the facts and details in paragraph 4. Ask yourself what most of these facts and details are about. That is the main idea. Use this information in your answer.

Independent Study

Directions: Answer the following questions on your own. For questions 4, 5, and 6, choose the correct answer. For question 7 you must write out your answer.

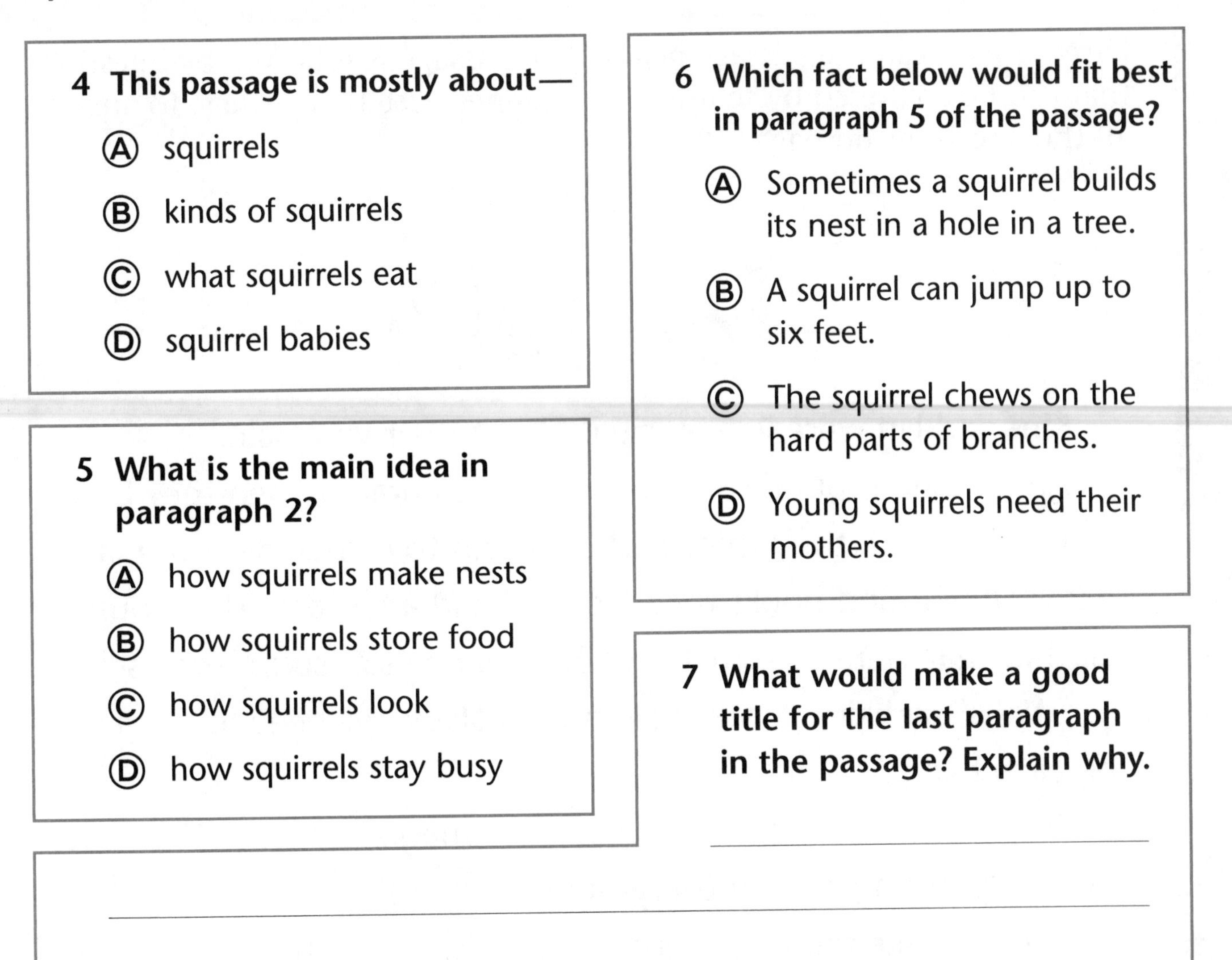

4 This passage is mostly about—

Ⓐ squirrels

Ⓑ kinds of squirrels

Ⓒ what squirrels eat

Ⓓ squirrel babies

5 What is the main idea in paragraph 2?

Ⓐ how squirrels make nests

Ⓑ how squirrels store food

Ⓒ how squirrels look

Ⓓ how squirrels stay busy

6 Which fact below would fit best in paragraph 5 of the passage?

Ⓐ Sometimes a squirrel builds its nest in a hole in a tree.

Ⓑ A squirrel can jump up to six feet.

Ⓒ The squirrel chews on the hard parts of branches.

Ⓓ Young squirrels need their mothers.

7 What would make a good title for the last paragraph in the passage? Explain why.

____

____

____

____

____

____

____

____

____

Skill 3: Sequence

Sequence is the order in which things or events happen. Things in the passage happen in a certain order. Each thing happens before, after, or at the same time as another thing.

Directions: Read the passage below. The passage is followed by questions that can be answered by telling the sequence. Use this passage to answer all the questions on pages 18–20.

For Sale

1 Kim and Lin were very excited about their yard sale.

2 First the girls found some boxes in the garage. Then they began to look through their things. They found toys they did not play with. They found books they did not read anymore. They found clothes that were too small. Lee had some craft supplies to sell.

3 "Wow!" said Kim. "Look at all this stuff! Now we need to put a price on each thing."

4 The girls found some tags. They got magic markers. Then they began to put a price on everything.

5 "Don't make the price very high," said Lee. "This is a yard sale. We want kids to be able to buy these things."

6 Most of the prices were low. Some things were 25 cents. Others were 50 cents. Lee put a tag on her craft supplies. It said $1.

7 "Now we need to make some signs," said Kim. "We want people to know when to come. They need to know where the sale is, too."

8 The girls found some cardboard and made signs.

9 They put the signs at each end of their street.

10 Lee said, "There is one more thing. We need to have some change. Look in your bank for quarters, nickels, and dimes. We should have some dollar bills, too."

11 The next day, the girls got up early. They put tables in the driveway. They set up their sale. They put money in a small box. People started to come.

12 "It's only 7:30!" said Kim. " Look at all the people!"

13 "Yes," said Lee. "People like to come early!"

14 "This is going to be a very good day," said Kim.

Modeled Instruction

Directions: You can answer this question by telling the sequence of the things that happen in the story. Read each answer. Use the strategy to choose the right answer.

1 What do the girls do first?

Ⓐ Make signs.

Ⓑ Find boxes.

Ⓒ Put money in a box.

Ⓓ Look through their things.

Strategy: A chart can help you answer a question about sequence. Read the story again. Put each thing that happens in the chart. Be sure you put them in order. Start with the first thing. Then put in the next thing. Finish the chart. Then answer the question.

Use this strategy to decide which answer is correct.

Ⓐ Make signs.

Look at your chart. You can see that the girls make signs later in the story. So, *choice "A" cannot be the correct answer.*

Ⓑ Find boxes.

Look at the first box in your chart. It should show that the girls find boxes. This is the first thing they do. So, *choice "B" must be the correct answer.*

Ⓒ Put money in a box.

Look at your chart. The girls put money in a box right before the sale starts. So, *choice "C" cannot be correct.*

Ⓓ Look through their things.

The girls look through their things near the beginning of the story. But your chart should show you that it is not the first thing they do. So, *choice "D" cannot be correct.*

Guided Instruction

Directions: Use the hints to answer the questions below. For question 2, you must choose the correct answer. For question 3, you will need to write out your answer.

2 Which of these happens after they put on the price tags?

Ⓐ Kim and Lin find boxes.

Ⓑ The girls get magic markers.

Ⓒ Kim and Lin find some toys to sell.

Ⓓ The girls put tables in the driveway.

Hint: Use your chart to answer this question. Ask yourself which thing happens first.

3 List three things that happen after the girls find boxes.

Hint: Use your chart. Look at all the things that happen after the girls find boxes.

Independent Study

Directions: Answer the following questions on your own. For questions 4, 5, and 6, choose the correct answer. For question 7, you must write out your answer.

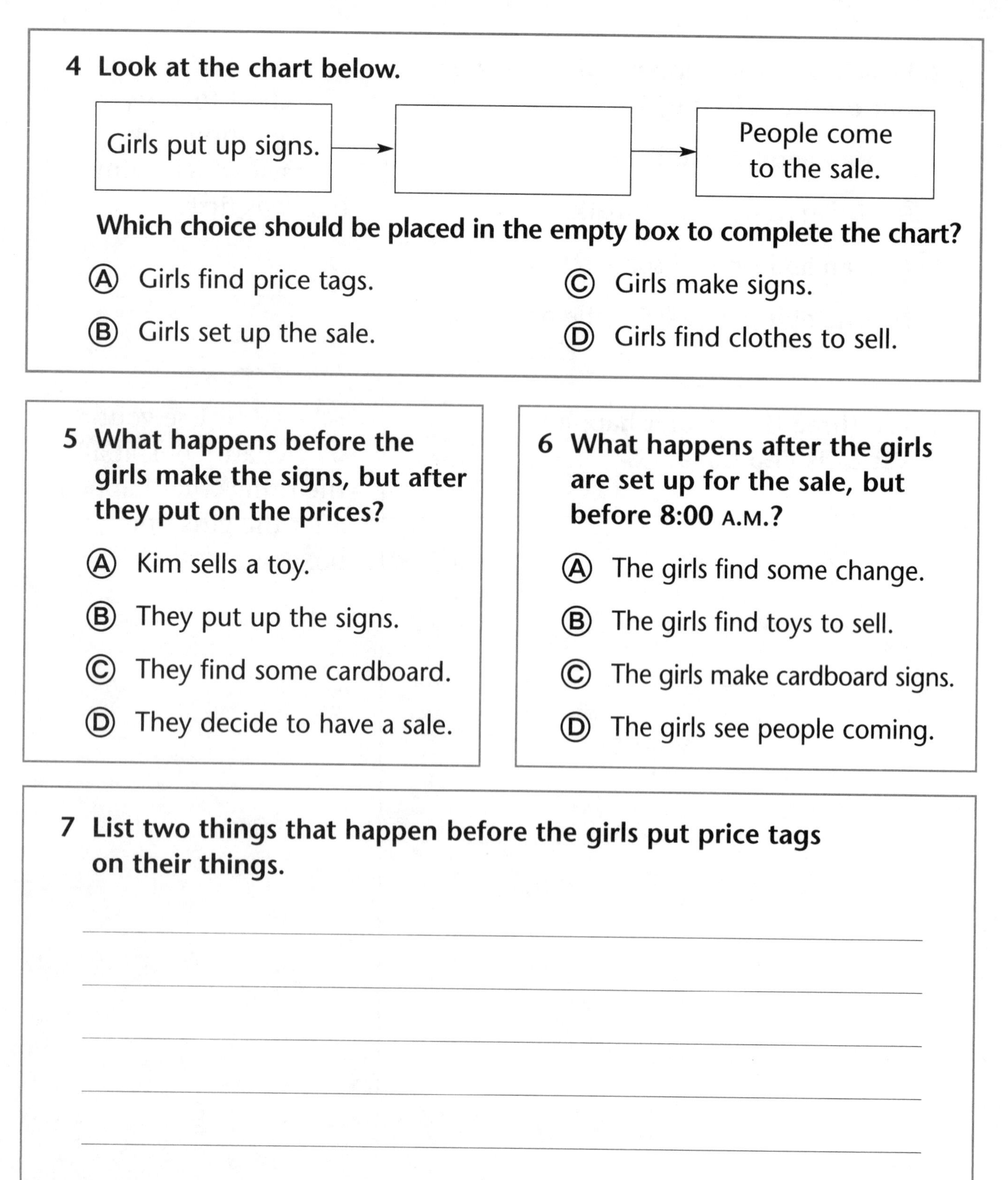

4 Look at the chart below.

Which choice should be placed in the empty box to complete the chart?

Ⓐ Girls find price tags.

Ⓑ Girls set up the sale.

Ⓒ Girls make signs.

Ⓓ Girls find clothes to sell.

5 What happens before the girls make the signs, but after they put on the prices?

Ⓐ Kim sells a toy.

Ⓑ They put up the signs.

Ⓒ They find some cardboard.

Ⓓ They decide to have a sale.

6 What happens after the girls are set up for the sale, but before 8:00 A.M.?

Ⓐ The girls find some change.

Ⓑ The girls find toys to sell.

Ⓒ The girls make cardboard signs.

Ⓓ The girls see people coming.

7 List two things that happen before the girls put price tags on their things.

Skill 4: Language and Vocabulary

Words, phrases, and sentences are used in every passage. Language is used to tell about ideas. Words and phrases have certain meanings. Sometimes there is more than one meaning. The meaning often depends on how the words are used.

Directions: Read the poem below. The poem is followed by questions that can be answered by thinking about the words, phrases, and sentences. Use this poem to answer all the questions on pages 23–24.

by Thomasin Heyworth

1 I love to swim in the deep blue sea,
2 With all those fishes looking at me.
3 Fishes in every possible *hue*—
4 Red ones, blue ones, and yellow ones, too.

5 They scatter quickly as I swim by,
6 They seem to *shimmer* like stars in the sky.
7 While lobsters—one, two, three, four—
8 Move slowly across the ocean floor.

9 Seaweeds wave as the waters flow,
10 The sun shines down on the shells below.
11 Clams, big and small, *move* with the tide,
12 In and out on an endless ride.

13 Good-bye little fishes, good-bye salty friends,
14 Once more my visit must come to an end.
15 Yes, I'd love to stay down below,
16 But up to dry land is where I must go!

U.S. Fish & Wildlife Service, Smallmouth Bass, Washington DC Library

Modeled Instruction

Directions: The question below can be answered by thinking about the words in the poem. Use the strategy to help choose the correct answer.

1 In line 3 the word *hue* means—

Ⓐ size

Ⓑ shape

Ⓒ sound

Ⓓ color

Strategy: Think about how the word is used in the passage. This can help you to understand its meaning. Sometimes other words in the passage can also give you clues about the meaning of the word. The word *hue* is in the first stanza, or part, of the poem. What words are in the rest of the sentence?

Use this strategy to decide which answer is correct.

Ⓐ size

The words *big* and *small* tell about size. But they are not in the same part of the poem as *hue*. They are in the last stanza. Therefore, *choice "A" is not correct.*

Ⓑ shape

There are no words in the poem that tell about shapes. Therefore, *choice "B" is not correct.*

Ⓒ sound

The poem does not tell about sounds in the sea. Therefore, *choice "C" is not correct.*

Ⓓ color

The other words in this sentence describe fish that are different colors. It makes sense that *hue* is another word for *color*. Therefore, *choice "D" is the correct answer.*

Guided Instruction

Directions: Use the hints to answer the questions below. For question 2, you must choose the correct answer. For question 3, you will need to write out your answer.

2 The phrase "They scatter so quickly as I swim by," seems to mean that—

Ⓐ the fish hide from the swimmer

Ⓑ the fish touch the swimmer

Ⓒ the fish hurry away from the swimmer

Ⓓ the fish try to follow the swimmer

Hint: Compare the group of words in each answer choice with the words in the question. Which answer choice has the same meaning as the words in the question?

3 What do you think the phrase "seaweeds wave as the waters flow" means?

____

____

____

____

____

____

____

____

____

____

____

____

Hint: Read the part of the poem where you see this phrase. What do the details tell you about what the poet can see? What is happening to the seaweeds?

Independent Study

Directions: Answer the following questions on your own. For questions 4, 5, and 6, choose the correct answer. For question 7, you must write out your answer.

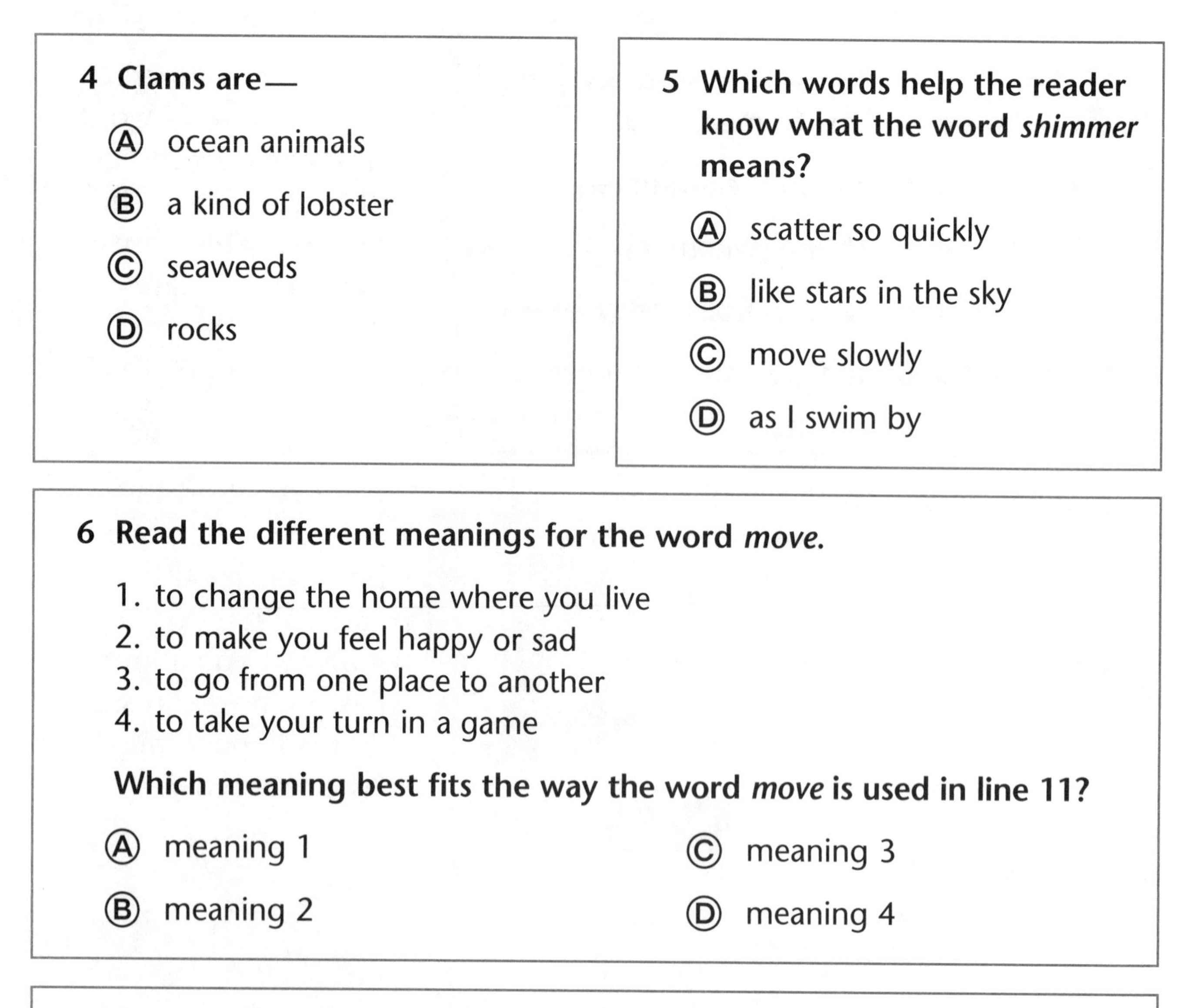

4 Clams are—

Ⓐ ocean animals

Ⓑ a kind of lobster

Ⓒ seaweeds

Ⓓ rocks

5 Which words help the reader know what the word *shimmer* means?

Ⓐ scatter so quickly

Ⓑ like stars in the sky

Ⓒ move slowly

Ⓓ as I swim by

6 Read the different meanings for the word *move*.

1. to change the home where you live
2. to make you feel happy or sad
3. to go from one place to another
4. to take your turn in a game

Which meaning best fits the way the word *move* is used in line 11?

Ⓐ meaning 1

Ⓑ meaning 2

Ⓒ meaning 3

Ⓓ meaning 4

7 In line 13, who are the salty friends? Why is that a good name for them?

Skill 5: Character, Plot, and Setting

These three things are found in every story.

CHARACTER	This is **who** the story is about.
PLOT	This is **what** the story is about.
SETTING	This is **where** and **when** the events in the story take place.

Directions: Read the passage below. It is followed by questions that can be answered by telling about the characters, plot, and setting. Use this story to answer all the questions on pages 27–29.

1 Jake tied Bo's leash around a bike rack on the sidewalk.

2 "Now you stay right there," he said. Jake gave his dog a pat on the head. Bo wagged his tail. He watched Jake walk into the store.

3 Jake picked up a basket. Then he took out her mother's list. He walked through the store. He found peanut butter. He found sugar. He put two sticks of butter his basket. He added a loaf of bread. He saw his favorite cookies. He decided not to buy the cookies. He would ask his mother later.

4 Jake went to the front of the store. He paid Mr. Green.

5 Mr. Green said. "Here is a bone for Bo." He put the bone in a small bag.

6 "Thank you," said Jake. "Bo will love this."

7 Jake left the store. "Oh, no!" he cried. Bo's leash was still on the bike rack. But Bo was gone! Jake often tied his dog to the rack. This had never happened before.

8 "Bo! Bo!" called Jake. "Have you seen my dog?" he asked everyone who passed. No one had seen Bo. Jake was afraid. What if Bo was hit by a car? Maybe someone took Bo. Jake walked up and down the block.

9 Jake could not find Bo. He walked home. He had the bag full of food. He had Bo's bone in the small bag. Bo's leash was in his hand. Jake walked slowly. He looked all around him. He hoped that he would find Bo. But he felt like he was going to cry.

10 Suddenly, he heard a sound. It was Bo's bark! Jake looked at his building. There on the front step was Bo. He wagged his tail. Then he ran to Jake.

11 "Bo, you silly dog!" cried Jake. He put down the bags and hugged him. "Next time you have to wait for me!"

12 "Woof!" said Bo. He sniffed at the small bag.

13 "Yes, Mr. Green gave you a bone," laughed Jake. "Here you go."

Modeled Instruction

Directions: This question can be answered by telling about the character, plot, or setting in the story. Use the strategy to help choose the correct answer.

1 Where does most of the story take place?

Ⓐ at Jake's house

Ⓑ at the bike rack

Ⓒ in and near the store

Ⓓ near the cookies

Strategy: Put the information about the story into a story map. The map shows who is in the story and what they do. It also shows where and when the story takes place. This question is asking you where the story takes place. This is a question about the setting of the story.

Use this strategy to decide which answer is correct.

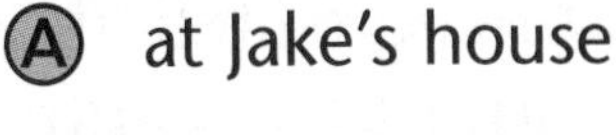

Ⓐ at Jake's house

Different events in the story happen in different places. But most of the events happen in one place. Only one part of the story takes place at Jake's house. Most of the story happens in other places. Therefore, *choice "A" cannot be correct.*

Ⓑ at the bike rack

Jake ties Bo up on the bike rack. And he goes there again to find that his dog is gone. But those are two short events. More of the story takes place somewhere else. Therefore, *choice "B" cannot be correct.*

Ⓒ in and near the store

Jake spends some time in the store. He also spends quite a lot of time near the store looking for Bo. This is more time than he spends in any other place. Therefore, *choice "C" must be the correct answer.*

Ⓓ near the cookies

Jake spends only a small amount of time near the cookies. Most of the story takes place away from the cookies. Therefore, *choice "D" cannot be correct.*

Guided Instruction

Directions: Use the hints to answer the questions below. For question 2, you must choose the correct answer. For question 3, you will need to write out your answer.

2 What can you tell about Jake and Bo from reading the passage?

Ⓐ They are good shoppers.

Ⓑ They like to eat bones.

Ⓒ They both like cookies.

Ⓓ They are good friends.

Hint: Think about what Jake and Bo do in the story. The things that characters do or say can tell you a lot about them. This is a character question.

3 Tell what this story is about. Tell what happens in the beginning, middle, and end of the story.

____

____

____

____

____

____

____

____

____

____

____

____

Hint: To tell the plot of a story, you only need to tell about important facts and events. Think about what information would be important to know. Do not tell every small detail.

Independent Study

Directions: Answer the following questions on your own. For questions 4, 5, and 6, choose the correct answer. For question 7, you must write out your answer.

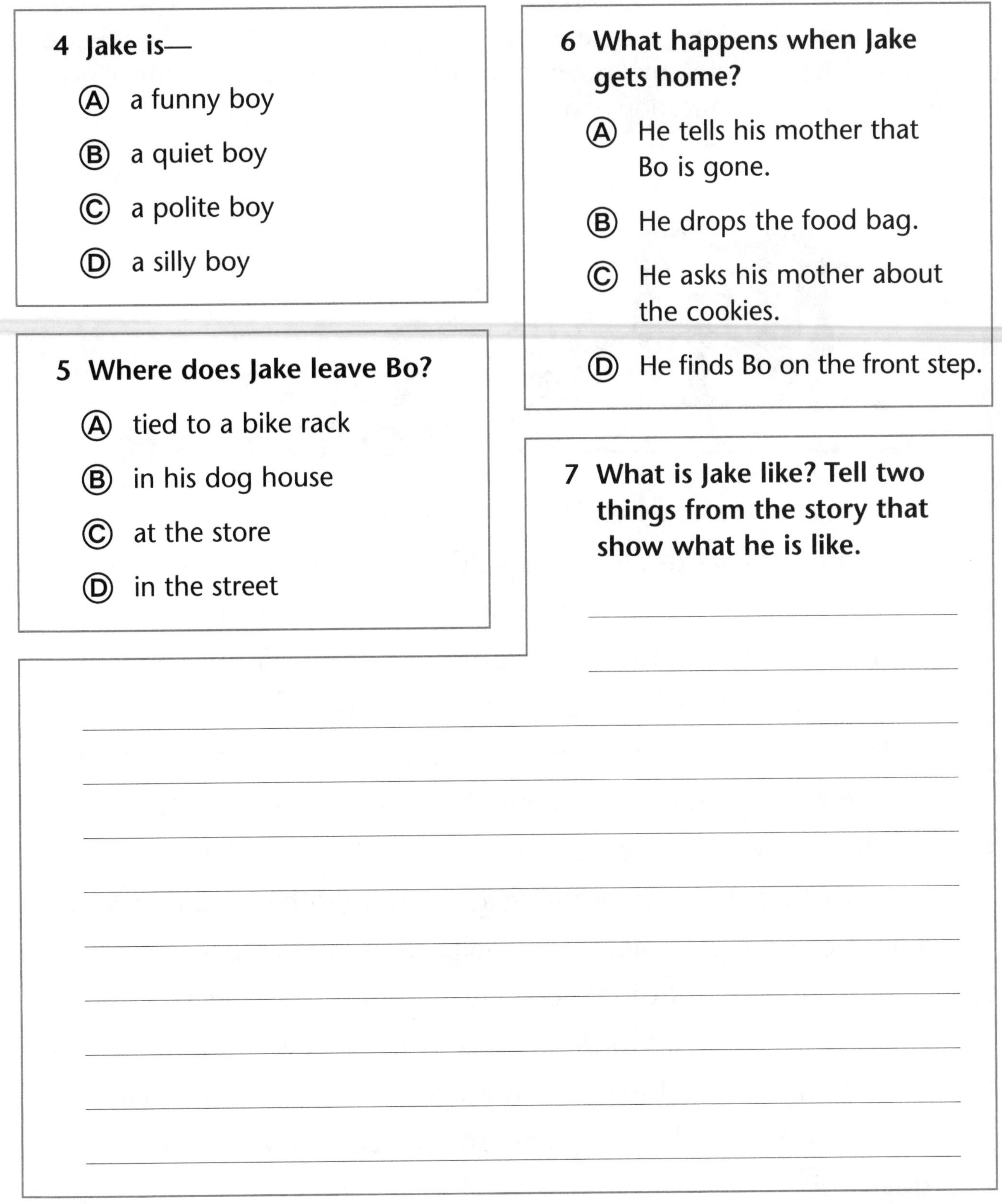

4 Jake is—

Ⓐ a funny boy

Ⓑ a quiet boy

Ⓒ a polite boy

Ⓓ a silly boy

5 Where does Jake leave Bo?

Ⓐ tied to a bike rack

Ⓑ in his dog house

Ⓒ at the store

Ⓓ in the street

6 What happens when Jake gets home?

Ⓐ He tells his mother that Bo is gone.

Ⓑ He drops the food bag.

Ⓒ He asks his mother about the cookies.

Ⓓ He finds Bo on the front step.

7 What is Jake like? Tell two things from the story that show what he is like.

Skill 6: Cause and Effect

The cause leads to the effect.

CAUSE *The wind blows hard.*
EFFECT *The tree falls down.*

Directions: Read the passage below. The passage is followed by questions that can be answered by knowing the cause and effect. Use this passage to answer all the questions on pages 32–34.

WHAT TO WEAR

1 You wear shorts when it is hot. When it is cold, you put on a sweater or a jacket. If it gets colder, you add a hat. You put on mittens. You feel good when you dress right. You stay cool or warm. But wearing the right clothes is not just about comfort. It is about your health, too. So dress smart!

2 Too much heat is not good for you. But there are things you can do to help your body. When it is very hot, try not to be in the sun too long. Spend some quiet time in the shade. Wear a hat. Wear clothes that are a light weight. Your clothes should also be a light color. Light colors stay cooler than dark colors.

3 When it is hot outside, you sweat. Your body loses water when you sweat. You need to drink more water to take its place. If you do not, you will feel sick. You may get a headache. You might feel dizzy. You could even faint. So take care of your body and stay cool.

4 Now think of cold weather. Are you thinking of winter? You can get very cold in the spring and fall, too. Wind can make the air colder. If you get wet, your body will get even colder.

5 Cold weather can be dangerous, too. When it is very cold, wear layers. Start with long underwear. Put a shirt and long pants over that. Add a heavy sweater. Wear a warm coat. Wool clothes are good in cold weather. Wool is warmer than cotton. It stays warm when it is wet. But if you get wet, it is a good idea to change into dry clothes.

6 Parts of your body that are not covered can get very cold. They can get so cold that they freeze. This is frostbite. Your fingers and toes can freeze. Your nose can freeze, too. Always wear gloves and warm socks. Wear boots. You lose a lot of heat through the top of your head. Wear a hat to hold in the heat. Some hats can also keep your ears warm. Wear a scarf to keep your nose, cheeks, and chin warm.

7 Dress for the weather. It is not just your mom's idea. It is a good idea!

Modeled Instruction

Directions: Below is an example of a question that can be answered by finding cause and effect. Use the strategy to help choose the correct answer.

1 What causes your body to lose water?

Ⓐ wearing wool

Ⓑ fainting

Ⓒ having headaches

Ⓓ sweating

Strategy: If the question gives the cause, look in the passage for the effect. If the question gives the effect, look for the cause. This question gives the effect: "loses water." What causes your body to lose water? Look for the words "loses water" in the story. Read that part of the story.

Use this strategy to decide which answer is correct.

Ⓐ wearing wool

The key words "loses water" are in paragraph 3. The paragraph about wearing wool is later in the passage. There are no details that say these two ideas go together. Therefore, *choice "A" cannot be correct.*

Ⓑ fainting

In paragraph 3, it says that heat might make you faint. But it does not say that fainting makes your body lose water. Therefore, *choice "B" cannot be correct.*

Ⓒ having headaches

The key words "loses water" and the word "headache" are all in paragraph 3. But the details do not say that headaches can make your body lose water. Therefore, *choice "C" is not correct.*

Ⓓ sweating

The key words "loses water" are in paragraph 3. The sentence with the key words tells you that when you sweat, your body loses water. Therefore, *choice "D" is the correct answer.*

Guided Instruction

Directions: Use the hints to answer the questions below. For question 2, you must choose the correct answer. For question 3, you will need to write out your answer.

2 If you do not wear a hat in cold weather—

Ⓐ your body will lose heat

Ⓑ you will get frostbite

Ⓒ you will get too much sun

Ⓓ your nose will get cold

Hint: Not wearing a hat is the cause of something. Look for the key words "wear a hat" in the passage. Read that part of the passage to find the information you need.

3 What can cause you to feel dizzy?

____

____

____

____

____

____

____

____

____

____

____

____

____

____

Hint: Feeling dizzy is the effect of something else that happens. Look through the passage to find the details that explain what causes this.

Independent Study

Directions: Answer the following questions on your own. For questions 4, 5, and 6, choose the correct answer. For question 7, you must write out your answer.

4 Clothes that are a dark color—

Ⓐ help you stay cool

Ⓑ help stop frostbite

Ⓒ get hotter than light colors

Ⓓ stay warm when they get wet

5 If you do not drink enough water—

Ⓐ you will sweat

Ⓑ you might feel sick

Ⓒ you might get frostbite

Ⓓ you will need a warm coat

6 If you dress for the weather—

Ⓐ you will never sweat

Ⓑ you will always wear layers

Ⓒ you will not need to drink water

Ⓓ you will be more comfortable

7 Why is wool better than cotton in cold weather? Give two reasons.

Skill 7: Compare and Contrast

Compare means to tell how things are alike. Contrast means to tell how things are different. You can compare and contrast people, places, or things that happen.

Directions: Read the passage below. The passage is followed by questions that can be answered by comparing or contrasting. Use this passage to answer all the questions on pages 37–39.

1 There are eleven students in Joey's reading group. Today they will make a chart. They will see how they are the same. And they will see how they are not alike.

2 Each student's name is on the chart. There is a list of traits. A trait is something about you. You might have brown hair. You might have blue eyes. You might be tall. You might be able to roll your tongue!

3 Mr. Carr is the teacher. He shows the students how to mark the chart. They fill it in. They check the spaces that tell about them. This is how the chart looks:

			HAIR				EYES			Can Roll	Can Wiggle
Student	**Girl**	**Boy**	**Brown**	**Black**	**Blond**	**Red**	**Brown**	**Blue**	**Green**	**Tongue**	**Ears**
Ali	√		√				√			√	√
Joey		√	√				√			√	√
Raven	√		√						√		
Peter		√				√			√	√	√
Clark		√	√						√	√	
Tia	√			√					√		√
Tyrone		√	√				√			√	√
Matt		√			√			√			√
Sara	√		√					√		√	√

4 Read the chart. The line across the top has the traits. Put your finger on Ali's name. Move your finger to the right. Stop when you see a check mark. Now look at the trait on the top line. The first mark tells you that Ali is a girl. The next mark is under brown hair. The next one is under brown eyes. The last mark shows that Ali can roll her tongue.

5 Raven sticks her tongue out. She wiggles it around. "Why can't I roll my tongue?" she asks.

6 "Some people can. And some can't. It is a trait you are born with," says Mr. Carr.

7 Ali rolls her tongue again. Peter wiggles his ears. Sara laughs. "I am glad you are having a good time," says Mr. Carr. "Let's see what this chart tells us."

Write your name in the first box.
Put a check mark under each of your traits.

My Name	Girl	Boy	HAIR				EYES			Can Roll Tongue	Can Wiggle Ears
			Brown	Black	Blond	Red	Brown	Blue	Green		

A Picture of Me

Modeled Instruction

Directions: Below is an example of a question that can be answered by comparing and contrasting information in the passage. Use the strategy to help choose the correct answer.

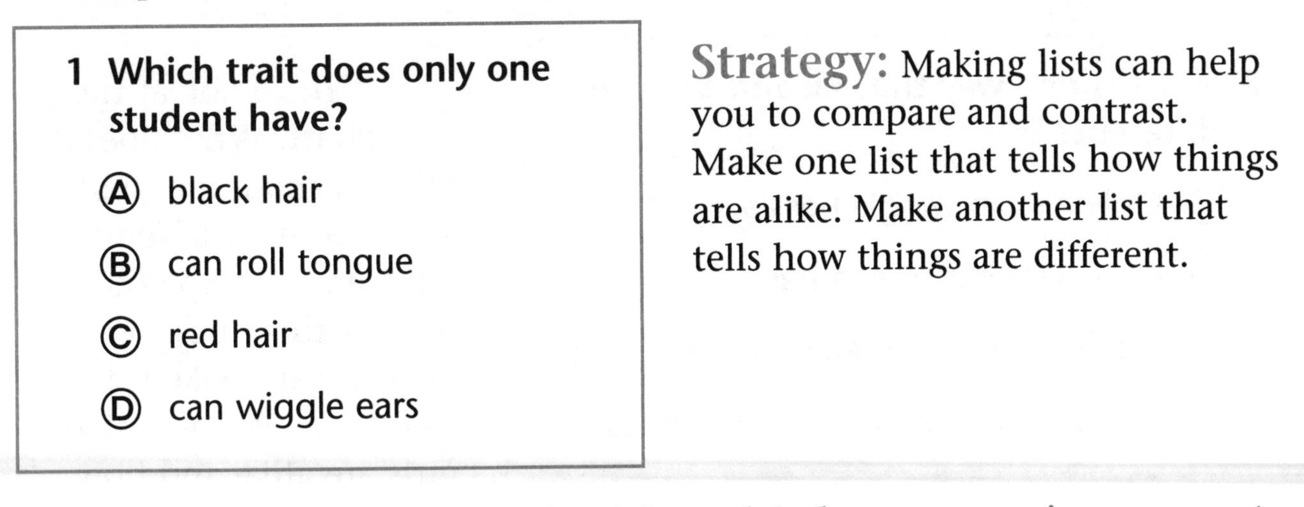

1 Which trait does only one student have?

Ⓐ black hair

Ⓑ can roll tongue

Ⓒ red hair

Ⓓ can wiggle ears

Strategy: Making lists can help you to compare and contrast. Make one list that tells how things are alike. Make another list that tells how things are different.

Use this strategy to decide which answer is correct.

Ⓐ black hair

Look at the chart. How many students have black hair? There are two students with black hair. These two students both have the same trait. So *choice "A" cannot be correct.*

Ⓒ red hair

You can see that there is only one check mark under red hair. Peter is the only student with this trait. Therefore, *choice "C" is the correct answer.*

Ⓑ can roll tongue

Use the chart. Six students can roll their tongue. So, *choice "B" cannot be correct.*

Ⓓ can wiggle ears

More than one student can wiggle their ears. Therefore, *choice "D" cannot be correct.*

Guided Instruction

Directions: Use the hints to answer the questions below. For question 2, you must choose the correct answer. For question 3, you will need to write out your answer.

2 What is one way that Ali and Sara are different?

Ⓐ Only Ali can wiggle her ears.

Ⓑ Only Sara has brown hair.

Ⓒ Sara has blue eyes and Ali has brown.

Ⓓ Sara can roll her tongue, but Ali can't.

Hint: Look at the chart. What does it tell you about the girls? You can make a Venn Diagram to help you answer this question. Or you can make lists that tell how these two girls are alike and how they are different.

3 How are Joey and Matt different?

____

____

____

____

____

____

____

____

____

____

____

____

Hint: Look at the chart. Read the information about each boy. Compare the details. Tell how the two are different.

Independent Study

Directions: Answer the following questions on your own. For questions 4, 5, and 6, choose the correct answer. For question 7, you must write out your answer.

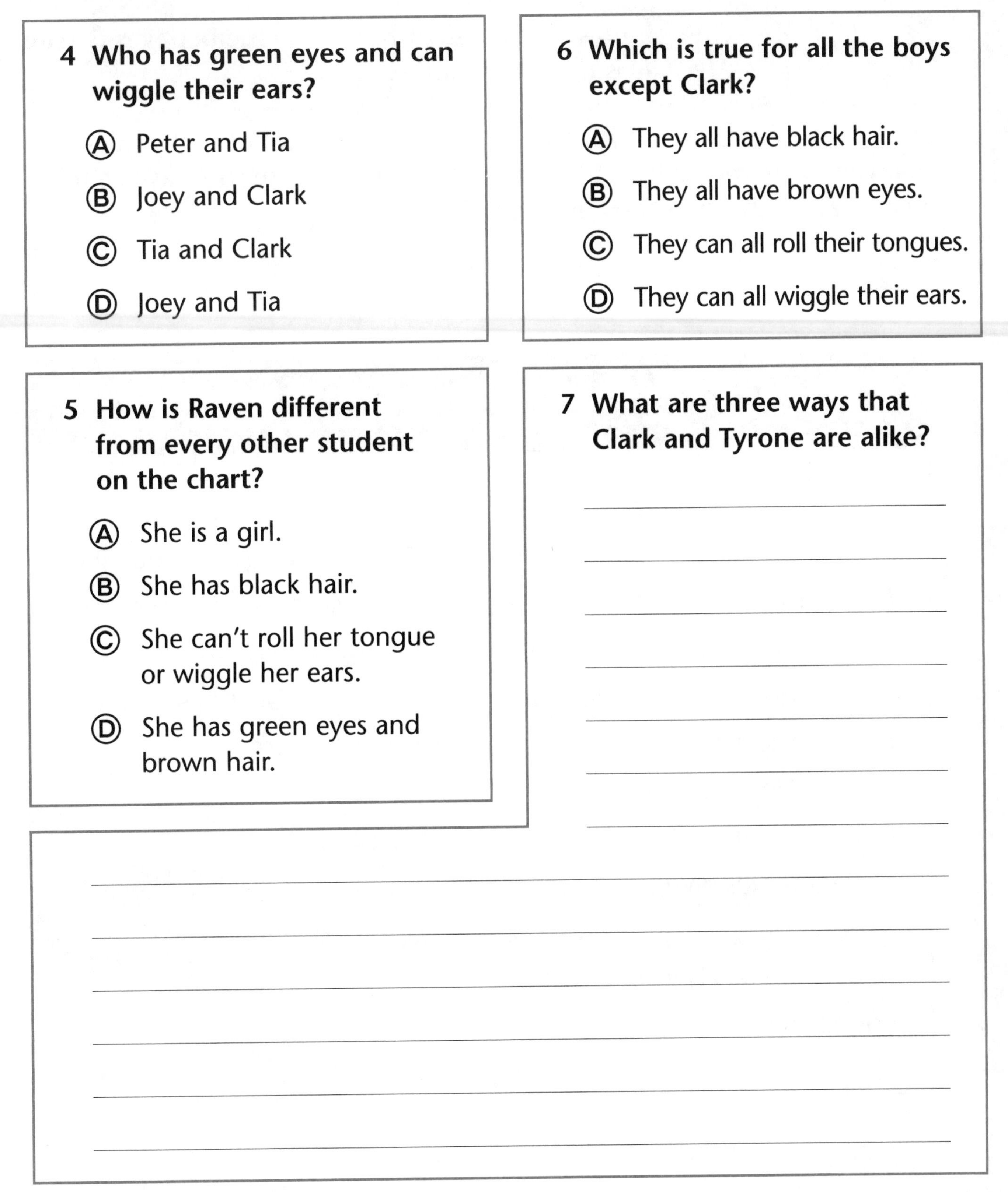

4 Who has green eyes and can wiggle their ears?

Ⓐ Peter and Tia

Ⓑ Joey and Clark

Ⓒ Tia and Clark

Ⓓ Joey and Tia

5 How is Raven different from every other student on the chart?

Ⓐ She is a girl.

Ⓑ She has black hair.

Ⓒ She can't roll her tongue or wiggle her ears.

Ⓓ She has green eyes and brown hair.

6 Which is true for all the boys except Clark?

Ⓐ They all have black hair.

Ⓑ They all have brown eyes.

Ⓒ They can all roll their tongues.

Ⓓ They can all wiggle their ears.

7 What are three ways that Clark and Tyrone are alike?

Skill 8: Facts and Opinions

It is important to be able to tell the difference between facts and opinions.

FACT A fact is a statement that **is true**.
There are 50 states in the United States.

OPINION An opinion is a statement that someone **believes is true**.
My state is the most beautiful.

Directions: Read the passage below. The passage is followed by questions that can be answered by telling fact from opinion. Use this passage to answer all of the questions on pages 42–44.

Good and Good for You

1 You eat meat and fish. You eat bread. You drink milk. But there is something else you should have every day. Listen now! Vegetables are good. And they are good for you! They can help your body in many ways.

2 Vegetables give you energy. Eating them makes you look better and feel better. It makes you strong!

3 There are many kinds, so you will find some you like. There is a vegetable for everyone! There are peas and peppers and beans. And there are many more.

4 Spinach and broccoli help your eyes. They are good for your skin, too. And they are good for your blood. Dark green foods like these are so good for you.

5 I think we all should eat broccoli. You already know some things it can do. It can also help if you have a cut. It helps your body heal.

6 Green beans and tomatoes help you grow. Tomatoes and peppers help you fight germs. Germs can make you sick. No one wants to be sick. It's much more fun to feel fine. Then you can play with your friends.

7 Do you want strong bones? Do you want a nice smile? Sweet potatoes and carrots can help. They make your bones and teeth strong.

8 You should eat vegetables every day. You do not have to be a cook. I love raw carrots. They are the best! You can eat carrots cooked or raw. Many vegetables taste good both ways.

9 Do you like peanut butter? Celery with peanut butter is the best snack. It makes me hungry just to think about it!

10 Try a bite of sweet potato. You will love it.Taste some peas. Taste a raw carrot.

11 Eat your vegetables! Your body will thank you. You will feel good. You will look good. It will make you smile!

Modeled Instruction

Directions: Below is an example of a question that can be answered by telling fact from opinion. Follow the strategy to help choose the correct answer.

1 Which of these is a fact?

Ⓐ Germs can make you sick.

Ⓑ Do you want a nice smile?

Ⓒ No one wants to be sick.

Ⓓ They are the best!

Strategy: Think about what you can prove. Statements that can be proven are facts. Statements that cannot be proven are opinions. What someone thinks or feels is true may not be true.

Use this strategy to decide which answer is correct.

think !

Ⓐ Germs can make you sick.

This statement tells something that we know is true. It has been proven that germs can make people sick. This is a fact. Therefore, *choice "A" must be the correct answer.*

think !

Ⓑ Do you want a nice smile?

This is a question. A question is not a fact or an opinion. Therefore, *choice "B" cannot be correct.*

think !

Ⓒ No one wants to be sick.

It seems that this statement would be true. No one wants to be sick. But you really cannot prove this. It is what the writer believes. It might be what you believe, too. But you can't prove that it is true or false. So it must be an opinion. Therefore, *choice "C" cannot be correct.*

think !

Ⓓ They are the best!

The writer thinks raw carrots are the best. There is no way to prove that everyone thinks so, too. Therefore, *choice "D" cannot be correct.*

Guided Instruction

Directions: Use the hints to answer the questions below. For question 2, you must choose the correct answer. For question 3, you will need to write out your answer.

2 Which sentence is an opinion?

Ⓐ Listen now!

Ⓑ You will love it.

Ⓒ You should eat vegetables every day.

Ⓓ They can help your body in many ways.

Hint: Read the answer choices one at a time. Ask yourself which statement you cannot prove. That statement is an opinion.

3 Read the following sentence:

"Celery with peanut butter is the best snack."

Is this a fact or an opinion? Explain your answer.

____

____

____

____

____

____

____

____

____

____

____

Hint: Think about what makes a statement a fact or an opinion. Ask yourself; is the statement something that **is true**? Can it be proven? Or is it something that someone **believes is true**?

Independent Study

Directions: Answer the following questions on your own. For questions 4, 5, and 6, choose the correct answer. For question 7, you must write out your answer.

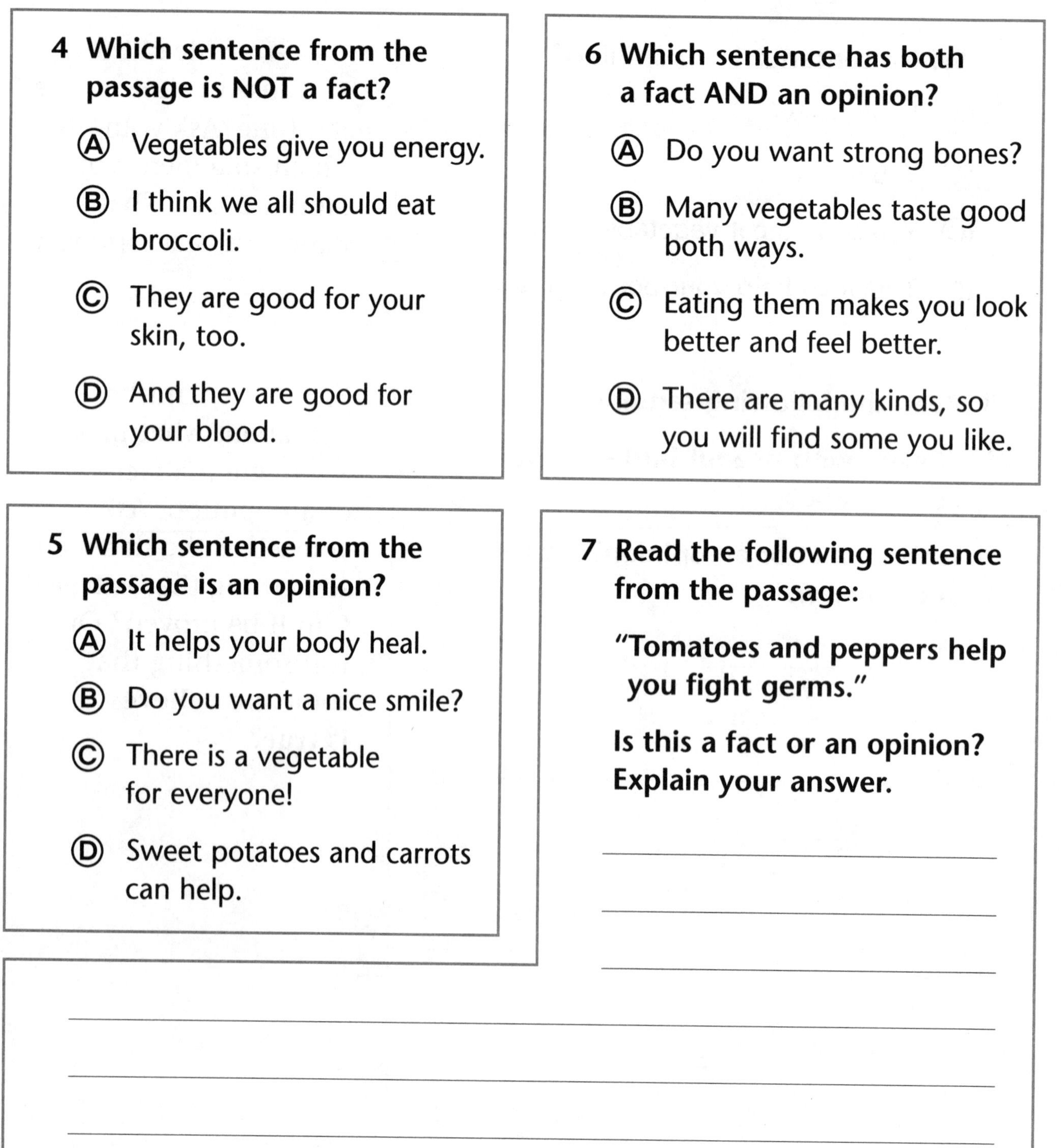

4 Which sentence from the passage is NOT a fact?

Ⓐ Vegetables give you energy.

Ⓑ I think we all should eat broccoli.

Ⓒ They are good for your skin, too.

Ⓓ And they are good for your blood.

5 Which sentence from the passage is an opinion?

Ⓐ It helps your body heal.

Ⓑ Do you want a nice smile?

Ⓒ There is a vegetable for everyone!

Ⓓ Sweet potatoes and carrots can help.

6 Which sentence has both a fact AND an opinion?

Ⓐ Do you want strong bones?

Ⓑ Many vegetables taste good both ways.

Ⓒ Eating them makes you look better and feel better.

Ⓓ There are many kinds, so you will find some you like.

7 Read the following sentence from the passage:

"Tomatoes and peppers help you fight germs."

Is this a fact or an opinion? Explain your answer.

Skill 9: Predict Outcomes

This means to figure out what will happen next or in the future. The exact information is not in the passage. But the facts and details may help tell what will happen.

Directions: Read the story below. The story is followed by questions that can be answered by predicting outcomes. Use this story to answer all of the questions on pages 47–49.

1 "Come on, Lee," called his mother. "We need to get to the store. The snow will start soon."

2 "Will we have school tomorrow?" asked Lee.

3 "I don't know. It is going to be a big storm."

4 "We are going to have a snow day!" Lee shouted.

5 "You don't know that yet!" laughed his mother. "Wait and see."

6 They went out to the car. The sky was dark and cloudy. A cold wind blew. Lee pulled his hat down over his ears. On the way to the store, he looked out the car window. Soon, everything would be white.

7 Lee had butterflies in his stomach. He was so excited! There might be a snow day. There would be no school. He could play in the snow all day. He had a new sled. His friend Pete had some tubes. They were so fast.

8 Lee thought about the hill. It was part of a sandpit. It was the best place in town to slide.

9 Sometimes the boys would slide all day. They got cold and wet. Then they would go home. There was a heat grate in the living room. Warm air came up from the cellar. It was the best place to put your cold feet. They got nice and warm. Lee's mother would make hot cocoa. Lee liked big marshmallows in his. Lee smiled. Coming home was almost as fun as sliding!

10 Lee's mother parked the car. There were a lot of people at the store.

11 "They must know about the snow, too," said Lee. "They're getting ready for a fun snow day!"

12 "And what if you do have school tomorrow?" said his mother, smiling.

13 "It can't happen! It is going to snow all night. Tomorrow will be a snow day for sure!"

Modeled Instruction

Directions: Below is a question that can be answered by using information from the story to predict an outcome. Use the strategy to help choose the correct answer.

1 What will Lee probably look for at the store?

Ⓐ a new toy

Ⓑ snow tubes and sleds

Ⓒ his friend

Ⓓ cocoa and marshmallows

Strategy: Find details in the passage that have something to do with the question. Decide what these details tell you about what will happen.

Use this strategy to decide which answer is correct.

Ⓐ a new toy

There are no details in the story about toys. So there is nothing to make you think that Lee would look for a toy. Therefore, *choice "A" cannot be correct.*

Ⓑ snow tubes and sleds

Details in the story tell that Pete has snow tubes. Lee thinks that he and Pete will use those snow tubes. And Lee has a new sled. So it does not make sense that he would look for more snow tubes or sleds. Therefore, *choice "B" cannot be correct.*

Ⓒ his friend

The story tells you that there are a lot of people at the store. But there are no details that would make you think Lee would look for his friend there. Therefore, *choice "C" cannot be correct.*

Ⓓ cocoa and marshmallows

The story tells you that Lee loves cocoa with marshmallows. You know that Lee wants his mother to make that on a snow day. You also know that the store is where she will get cocoa and marshmallows. Therefore, *choice "D" must be correct.*

Guided Instruction

Directions: Use the hints to answer the questions below. For question 2, you must choose the correct answer. For question 3, you will need to write out your answer.

2 You can tell that Lee will probably—

Ⓐ use a snow tube today

Ⓑ not have to go to school tomorrow

Ⓒ stay home from school for three days

Ⓓ drink all the cocoa when he gets home

Hint: Look for details in the story that tell you what Lee is thinking about. What do the details tell you will probably happen?

3 Where will most of the kids in town probably slide? Use details from the passage to support your answer.

____

____

____

____

____

____

____

____

____

____

____

____

____

Hint: Read the parts of the passage that talk about sliding. Use these details to help you figure out where the kids would go.

Independent Study

Directions: Answer the following questions on your own. For questions 4, 5, and 6, choose the correct answer. For question 7, you must write out your answer.

4 If there is a snow day, you can tell that—

Ⓐ Lee and Pete will probably go sliding together.

Ⓑ Lee and Pete will probably play video games.

Ⓒ Lee and Pete will probably go to the store.

Ⓓ Lee and Pete will probably stay inside.

5 What will Lee probably do after he goes sliding?

Ⓐ go to school

Ⓑ drink some milk

Ⓒ go to Pete's house

Ⓓ sit by the heat grate

6 What is the first thing Lee will probably do when he wakes up in the morning?

Ⓐ He will read a book.

Ⓑ He will drink hot cocoa.

Ⓒ He will ask if it is a snow day.

Ⓓ He will get dressed for school.

7 What will Pete and Lee use to slide on if there is a snow day? Use details from the passage to support your answer.

Skill 10: Reach Conclusions

Conclusions are based on facts found in the passage. Decisions are made about what the facts mean.

Directions: Read the passage below. The passage is followed by questions that can be answered by reaching conclusions. Use this passage to answer all of the questions on pages 52–54.

What's Up, Doc?

1 He is gray and white. He has long ears and huge feet. He has big, long teeth. He has a fluffy white tail. And he loves carrots! Who is he? He is Bugs Bunny. And he might be the best-known cartoon there is.

2 How old do you think he is? Bugs is over sixty years old! People saw Bugs Bunny in his first cartoon many years ago.

3 There was a rabbit in those first cartoons. The man who made that first rabbit cartoon was called "Bugs." Bugs Bunny might have been named after that man.

4 The first rabbit was smart. And he made a lot of trouble. Bugs Bunny is still like that. But the first rabbit was not quite the same Bugs Bunny we know. That first rabbit was all white. His face was different. And he was not very lovable.

5 The first rabbit had a different voice. Then Mel Blanc became the voice of Bugs Bunny. Mel's voice made Bugs more fun. It made people like Bugs more.

6 Have you seen Bugs Bunny on TV? He gets into a lot of trouble. But he always gets out somehow. He is smarter than everyone else. Elmer Fudd and Daffy Duck can never beat Bugs!

7 Bugs Bunny wants to be left alone. He wants to sit in his rabbit hole and eat carrots. But the others just will not let him. That is when the trouble starts. You might think the others would give up. But they keep trying. Bugs can be a very naughty rabbit. But we still want him to win. And he always does.

8 Bugs Bunny was a movie star first. Later, he was on TV. Other cartoons have come and gone. They did not last. But Bugs is still here. He even has his own show on TV. It is called "The Bugs Bunny Show."

9 Will people still watch Bugs years from now? Will they laugh at these cartoons? Who knows? But we do know one thing. People will not forget Bugs Bunny!

Modeled Instruction

Directions: Below is an example of a question that can be answered by drawing conclusions. Use the strategy to help choose the correct answer.

1 Why do you think people called the man "Bugs"?

Ⓐ It was his nickname.

Ⓑ He bothered them.

Ⓒ It was his real name.

Ⓓ He looked like a rabbit.

Strategy: Think about all the facts in the passage. Decide what the facts tell you.

Use this strategy to decide which answer is correct.

Ⓐ It was his nickname.

The details say that people called him "Bugs." If people do not use your real name, they usually use a nickname. From this you can conclude that *choice "A" must be the correct answer.*

Ⓑ He bothered them.

There are very few details about the man who made the first cartoon. There is nothing in the passage that tells how people felt about him. From this you can decide for yourself, that *choice "B" cannot be correct.*

Ⓒ It was his real name.

The man's name could have been Bugs. But the passage does not say Bugs was his name. It says that this is what people called him. From this you can conclude that *choice "C" cannot be correct.*

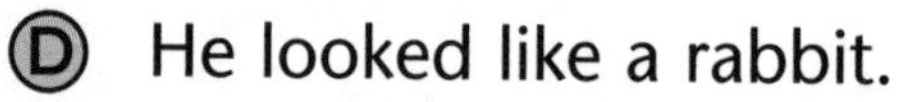

Ⓓ He looked like a rabbit.

People called the man "Bugs" before he drew the Bugs Bunny cartoon. So there was no reason to call him "Bugs" even if he did look like a rabbit. From this you can conclude that *choice "D" cannot be correct.*

Guided Instruction

Directions: Use the hints to answer the questions below. For question 2, you must choose the correct answer. For question 3, you will need to write out your answer.

2 You can conclude that people still love Bugs Bunny because—

Ⓐ they buy pet rabbits

Ⓑ they go to the movies

Ⓒ they watch his cartoons

Ⓓ they call their friends "Bugs"

Hint: Find details in the passage that tell about Bugs Bunny cartoons. Ask yourself what you can tell from this information.

3 Why do you think the first bunny did not sound like Bugs does today?

____
____
____
____
____
____
____
____
____
____
____
____
____

Hint: Think about what the passage says about Bugs' voice. What would make his voice different?

Independent Study

Directions: Answer the following questions on your own. For questions 4, 5, and 6, choose the correct answer. For question 7, you must write out your answer.

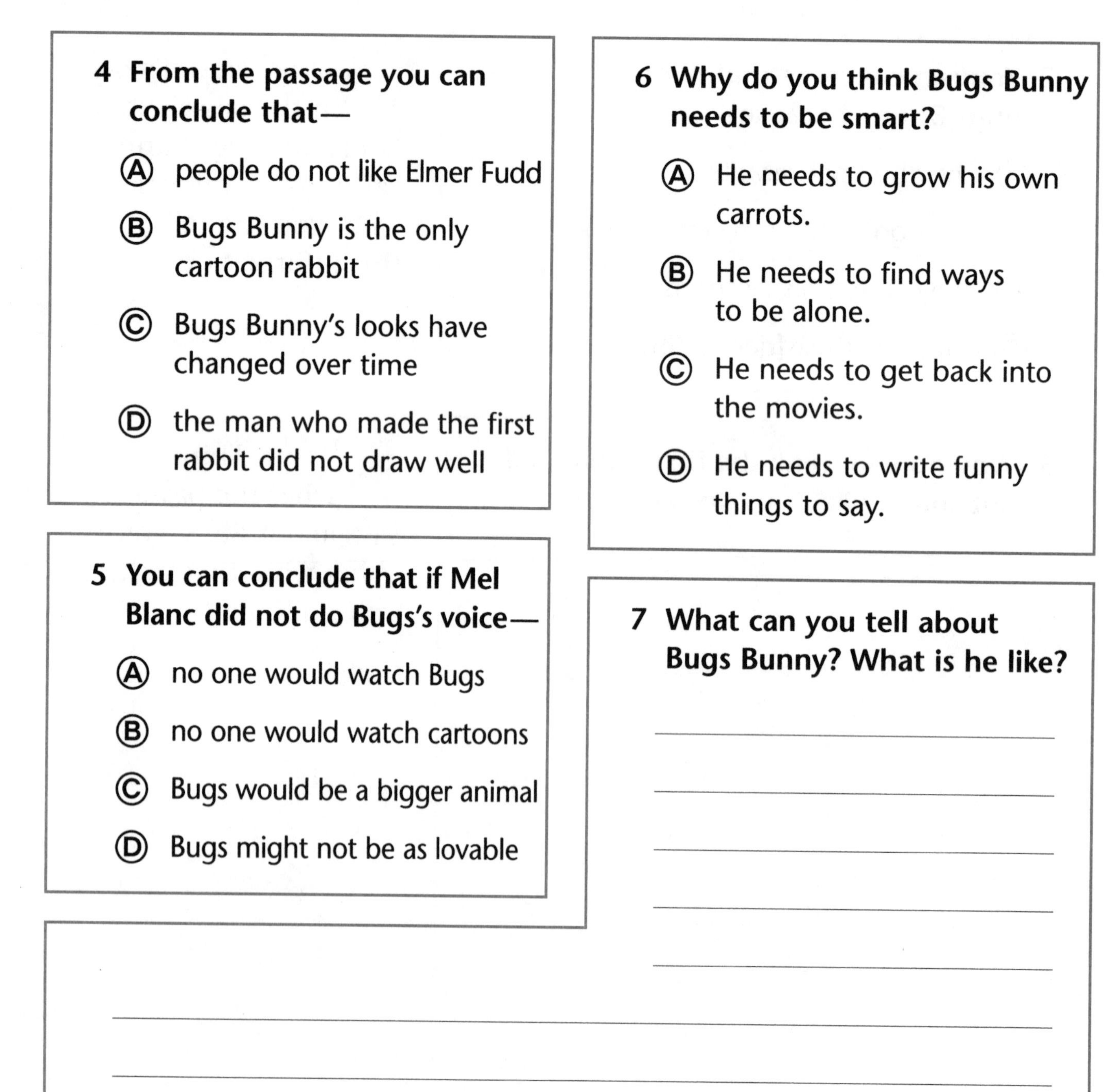

4 From the passage you can conclude that—

Ⓐ people do not like Elmer Fudd

Ⓑ Bugs Bunny is the only cartoon rabbit

Ⓒ Bugs Bunny's looks have changed over time

Ⓓ the man who made the first rabbit did not draw well

5 You can conclude that if Mel Blanc did not do Bugs's voice—

Ⓐ no one would watch Bugs

Ⓑ no one would watch cartoons

Ⓒ Bugs would be a bigger animal

Ⓓ Bugs might not be as lovable

6 Why do you think Bugs Bunny needs to be smart?

Ⓐ He needs to grow his own carrots.

Ⓑ He needs to find ways to be alone.

Ⓒ He needs to get back into the movies.

Ⓓ He needs to write funny things to say.

7 What can you tell about Bugs Bunny? What is he like?

Skill 11: Make Inferences

An inference is what is most likely to be true. It is an opinion based on information in the passage. Information may include maps, charts, pictures, and photos. Inferences are not always correct.

INFORMATION *Ann is ill.*
INFERENCE *She will not go to school tomorrow.*

Directions: Read the passage below. Look at the chart. The passage and chart are followed by questions that can be answered by making inferences. Use this information to answer all of the questions on pages 57–59.

1 Miss Shaw is a teacher at Pine School. She teaches spelling and math. She teaches science. She teaches reading. She also teaches about cleaning up. Miss Shaw does not make one day clean-up day. She makes every day clean-up day. Her students clean up all the time!

2 "Keep a plastic bag with you. If you see trash, put it in your bag. Then bring it to class and put it in the correct bin," says Miss Shaw.

3 There are four large bins. They sit outside the classroom. The students bring in the trash they collect. They put it into the bins. There is one for all kinds of paper. Writing paper, cardboard, candy wrappers, and other papers go in there. There is one for glass and one for plastic. And there is a bin for cans. The students pick up trash on the way to school. They pick it up at ball games. They pick it up in the playground. They pick up trash everywhere they go. The bins are getting full.

4 "If I see trash on the ground," says Joe, "I have to pick it up! I can't leave it there. It's a habit now!"

5 This makes Miss Shaw happy. She wanted her class to make cleaning up a habit.

6 Now it is May. The class has made a chart. It is called a pie chart. It shows how much of each kind of trash they have. The chart has four sections. There is one for each bin.

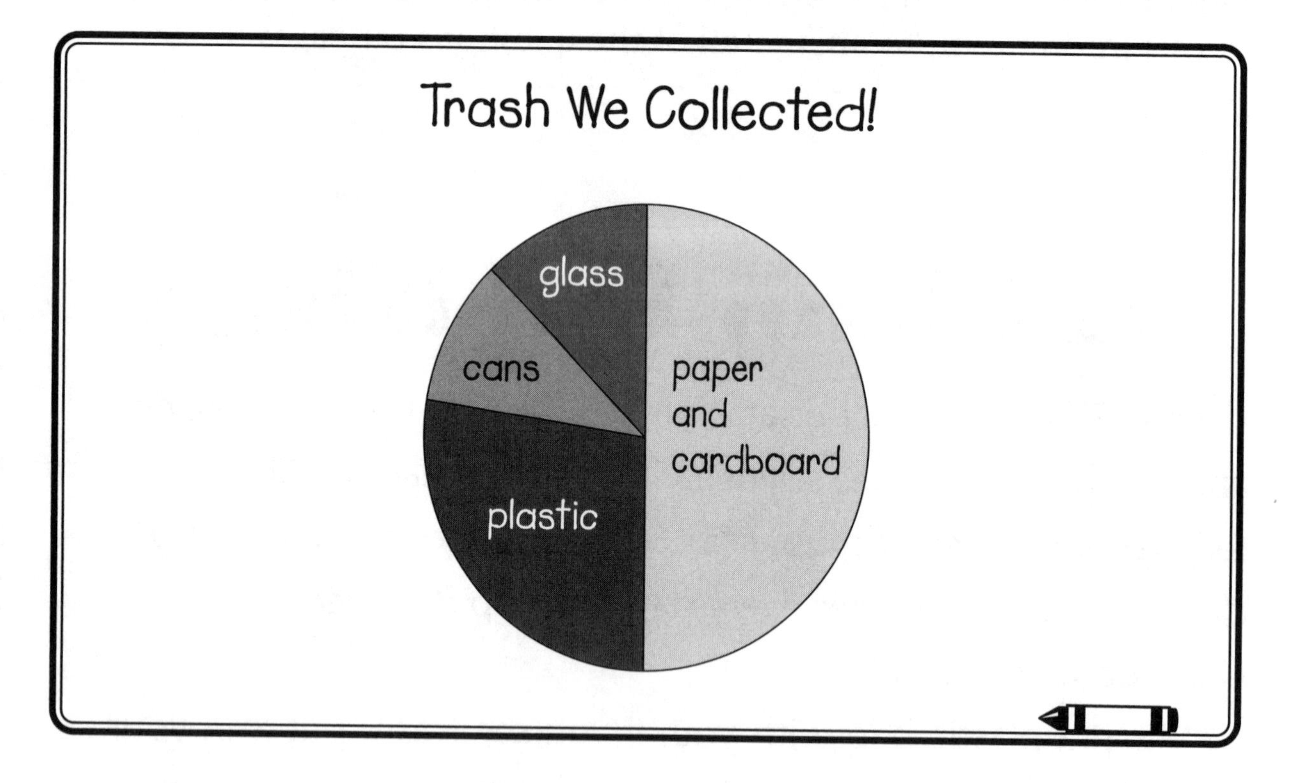

7 "I am proud of you. You have all done a great job. You worked all year," says Miss Shaw. "And our town looks nice. Now let's look at the chart. What does it say?"

Modeled Instruction

Directions: Below is an example of a question that can be answered by making inferences about the passage. Use the strategy to help choose the correct answer.

1 If Miss Shaw saw trash on the ground, she would probably—

Ⓐ tell Joe where she saw it

Ⓑ leave it there

Ⓒ ask a student to pick it up

Ⓓ pick it up herself

Strategy: Look at each answer choice. Find details in the passage about each answer. Decide which answer makes the most sense to you.

Use this strategy to decide which answer is correct.

Ⓐ tell Joe where she saw it

The details in the passage tell you that Joe does not like to leave trash on the ground. But Joe is not the only person who can pick up trash. So, *choice "A" does not make the most sense.*

Ⓑ leave it there

Miss Shaw is teaching her class to pick up trash. She feels strongly that trash should not be left on the ground. So, *choice "B" does not make the most sense.*

Ⓒ ask a student to pick it up

All of Miss Shaw's students have been picking up trash. But it does not make sense for Miss Shaw to leave the trash until she sees a student. So, *choice "C" does not make the most sense.*

Ⓓ pick it up herself

The details tell you that Miss Shaw feels that trash should be picked up. She probably wants to be a good example for her students. It makes sense that if she saw trash on the ground, she would pick it up herself. So, *choice "D" would be the best answer to this question.*

Guided Instruction

Directions: Use the hints to answer the questions below. For question 2, you must choose the correct answer. For question 3, you will need to write out your answer.

2 Which bin had the most trash in it?

Ⓐ the plastic bin

Ⓑ the paper bin

Ⓒ the glass bin

Ⓓ the can bin

Hint: Look at the chart. Look at the sizes of the different sections. Which section is the largest? What can you tell from this information?

3 Joe says that a picking up trash is a habit. What does he mean?

____

____

____

____

____

____

____

____

____

____

____

____

____

Hint: Think about what the details in the passage tell you. What do you do that is a habit? How can picking up trash be a habit?

Independent Study

Directions: Answer the following questions on your own. For questions 4, 5, and 6, choose the correct answer. For question 7, you must write out your answer.

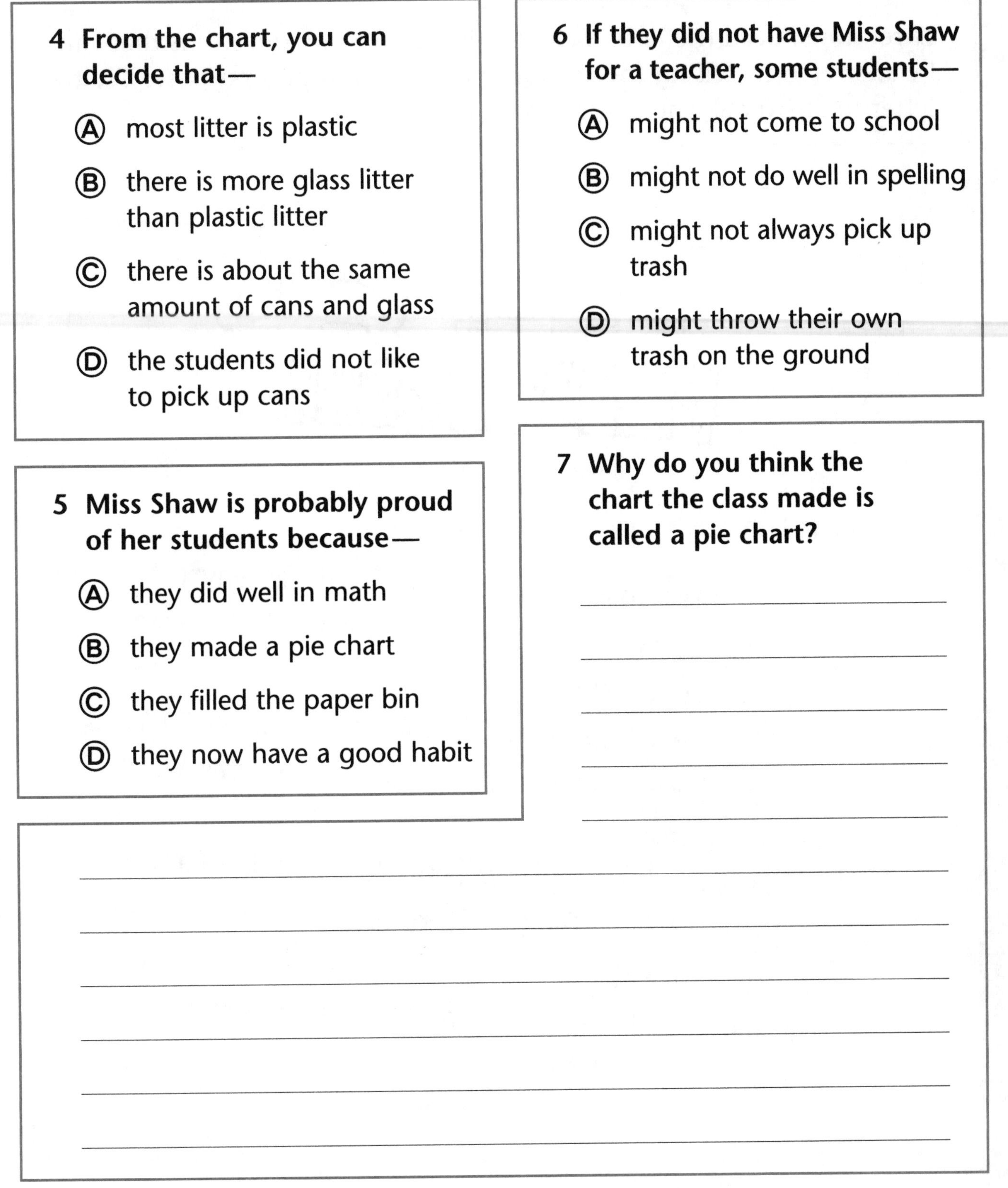

4 From the chart, you can decide that—

Ⓐ most litter is plastic

Ⓑ there is more glass litter than plastic litter

Ⓒ there is about the same amount of cans and glass

Ⓓ the students did not like to pick up cans

5 Miss Shaw is probably proud of her students because—

Ⓐ they did well in math

Ⓑ they made a pie chart

Ⓒ they filled the paper bin

Ⓓ they now have a good habit

6 If they did not have Miss Shaw for a teacher, some students—

Ⓐ might not come to school

Ⓑ might not do well in spelling

Ⓒ might not always pick up trash

Ⓓ might throw their own trash on the ground

7 Why do you think the chart the class made is called a pie chart?

Skill 12: Point of View and Purpose

Every author has a point of view and a purpose.

POINT OF VIEW This is what an author believes about something.
PURPOSE This is the reason why the author wrote the passage.

Directions: Read the letter below. It is followed by questions that can be answered by telling the author's point of view and purpose. Use this letter to answer all the questions on pages 62–64.

Dear Erin,

1 I really miss you! I hope you visit soon. Or maybe I will come to your house. But I think it would be more fun if you come here.

2 I did not want to move. I loved living in the country. But now I know that the city is fun, too. In some ways, it is even better!

3 I can walk from my new home to all kinds of places. And I can ride my bike, too. There are a lot of toy stores here. And the parks are so big. There are three of them! They have jungle gyms like you have never seen! I want to show you all of them.

4 There is a museum just for kids. We have been there a few times. Each time we go we visit a different part. My favorite part is the one about airplanes. You can be the pilot. It looks as if you are really flying!

5 There are many good places to eat here. I love the pizza places. There are some great hamburger places, too! But my favorite is a place with Greek food. There's a bakery on my block that sells wonderful bread. And there is a candy store nearby. It has every kind of candy you can think of.

6 There are things I miss. There are trees in the parks. But there is no place like the woods we used to play in. There's a lake in the park. But I miss the ocean. Still, there are many things to do and see here!

7 Ask your mom if you can come soon. You can stay for a few days. I will show you everything!

Your friend,
Kimi

Modeled Instruction

Directions: Below is an example of a question that can be answered by thinking about the author's point of view and purpose. Use the strategy to help choose the correct answer.

1 Kimi probably believes that—

Ⓐ most trees grow in the city

Ⓑ the city has better museums

Ⓒ there are more children in the city

Ⓓ there is more to do in the city than in the country

Strategy: Think about all the information in the passage. If you only think about a few details, you may not understand what the author believes or is trying to say.

Use this strategy to decide which answer is correct.

think !

Ⓐ most trees grow in the city

Kimi says that there are trees in the parks. But she also says that there are not as many there as there are in the woods in the country. Therefore, *choice "A" cannot be correct.*

Ⓑ the city has better museums

Kimi does talk about a museum near her house. She says she enjoys it. But this does not mean she thinks it is better than museums in the country. There is no way to know this. Therefore, *choice "B" cannot be correct.*

think !

Ⓒ there are more children in the city

There might be more children in the city. But Kimi does not talk about how many children there are. There is no way to know what she thinks about this. Therefore, *choice "C" cannot be correct.*

think !

Ⓓ there is more to do in the city than in the country

Kimi writes about all the things there are to do in the city. She says that in some ways, living in the city is better. She wants to share all there is to do with Erin. Therefore, *choice "D" is the correct answer.*

Guided Instruction

Directions: Use the hints to answer the questions below. For question 2, you must choose the correct answer. For question 3, you will need to write out your answer.

2 The author of this letter would most likely agree that—

Ⓐ people should stay in the country

Ⓑ the city is a good place to live

Ⓒ it is better to walk than to ride your bike

Ⓓ the country is the best place to live

Hint: Think about each answer choice. Look for details in the letter about each answer. Which choice is **best** supported by the details you can find?

3 Where can Kimi take Erin to eat? Where are they sure to go?

____

____

____

____

____

____

____

____

____

____

____

____

____

Hint: Think about things from Kimi's point of view. What does she say about food? What places to eat are near her house?

Independent Study

Directions: Answer the following questions on your own. For questions 4, 5, and 6, choose the correct answer. For question 7, you must write out your answer.

4 Kimi's main purpose for writing this letter is—

Ⓐ to tell Erin about her new home

Ⓑ to get Erin to move to the city

Ⓒ to tell Erin that she misses the country

Ⓓ to make Erin wish she lived in the city

5 Which of these is NOT what the author thinks?

Ⓐ Erin would enjoy visiting the city.

Ⓑ It is good to be able to walk to many places.

Ⓒ Going to the lake is more fun than going to the ocean.

Ⓓ The candy store near her house has all kinds of candy.

6 Which of the following does the author believe to be true?

Ⓐ Erin is not a good friend.

Ⓑ Everyone should live in the city.

Ⓒ It will take many visits to see everything in the kids' museum.

Ⓓ Pizza and hamburgers are the best things to eat in the city.

7 Give two reasons why Kimi likes living in her new home.

A Skill 13: Literary Forms and Sources of Information

There are different forms of writing. For example, a poem is different from a story. There are different sources of information. For example, information about current events is found in a newspaper.

Directions: The passage is followed by questions that can be answered by being able to tell one type of writing from another and by knowing where to find different kinds of writing. Use this passage to answer all of the questions on pages 67–69.

1 "Would you like to hear a story?" Mrs. Mark asked the children.

2 "What kind?" asked Lin. "I like stories with dragons and kings and queens."

3 "That would be a fairy tale," said Mrs. Mark. "Would you like one of those?"

4 "How about a story with space aliens? That is what I like." said Ben.

5 "That is science fiction," said Mrs. Mark. "Would anyone like to hear a fable?"

6 "Like the one with the crow and the fox?" asked Paul. "The crow learns not to listen to the fox. He loses his food when he sings!"

7 "Yes," Mrs. Mark answered. "The fox told the crow he had a nice voice. But he only wanted the crow to open his mouth. The crow dropped the grapes and the fox got them. Fables always teach a lesson. And they are about animals who can talk."

8 "It was fun when we acted out the story about the funny family," laughed Jenny.

9 "That's called a play," Paul said.

10 Mrs. Mark smiled, "Yes, that's what it is called."

11 "I liked your story about the dogs," said Paul. "Did that really happen?"

12 "No," laughed Mrs. Mark. "I made it all up. So it is called fiction. But it could really happen. So it is called realistic fiction. What kind of story is in a newspaper?"

13 "News!" yelled Lin. "Those are things that really happen. They don't just seem real. They are real."

14 "That's right!" said Mrs. Mark. "Now listen to this."

So much to read, so much to hear,
But you may choose just one, my dear.

15 The children laughed, "You choose, Mrs. Mark! Your stories are always good."

16 "Then I will tell you a new one," said Mrs. Mark. "This one is about a good dragon. He saves a village. But first the dragon must break a spell. Once upon a time, in a land far away..."

Modeled Instruction

Directions: Below is an example of a question that can be answered by telling apart different kinds of writing and telling where you might find different types of writing. Use the strategy to help choose the correct answer.

1 This whole passage is an example of—

Ⓐ poetry

Ⓑ a fairy tale

Ⓒ realistic fiction

Ⓓ a news story

Strategy: Ask yourself these questions:

- Why would you read this passage?
- How is the passage written? What is its style?
- What kind of information is in the passage?

Use this strategy to decide which answer is correct.

think !

Ⓐ poetry

In a poem the ends of many lines often rhyme. This does not describe the whole passage. Based on this information, *choice "A" is not correct.*

think !

Ⓑ a fairy tale

A fairy tale is a story that tells about things that could not really happen. The stories are often magical. A fairy tale often starts with "Once upon a time." The things that happen in fairy tales are unbelievable. Since this does NOT describe the whole passage, *choice "B" cannot be the answer.*

think !

Ⓒ realistic fiction

Realistic fiction tells about things that could really happen. The people in the story are not real. The things that happen did not really happen. But they seem real. Therefore, *choice "C" must be the correct answer.*

think !

Ⓓ a news story

A news story is about an event. The event is something that many people want to know about. The news story tells what happened, who was there, when it happened, and how it happened. Since this does NOT quite describe the passage, *choice "D" is not the best answer.*

Guided Instruction

Directions: Use the hints to answer the questions below. For question 2, you must choose the correct answer. For question 3, you will need to write out your answer.

2 The purpose of this passage is—

Ⓐ to help you write a play

Ⓑ to tell you a story

Ⓒ to get you to do something

Ⓓ to tell you about fables

Hint: Think about why the passage was probably written. Why might someone choose to read this passage?

3 Explain how you can tell that this passage is NOT an example of a news story.

____

____

____

____

____

____

____

____

____

____

____

____

____

Hint: A news story tells about real events. It tells who, what, where, when, and how. Its purpose is to tell people what is happening in the world around them. Think about how this compares to the passage you read.

Independent Study

Directions: Answer the following questions on your own. For questions 4, 5, and 6, choose the correct answer. For question 7, you must write out your answer.

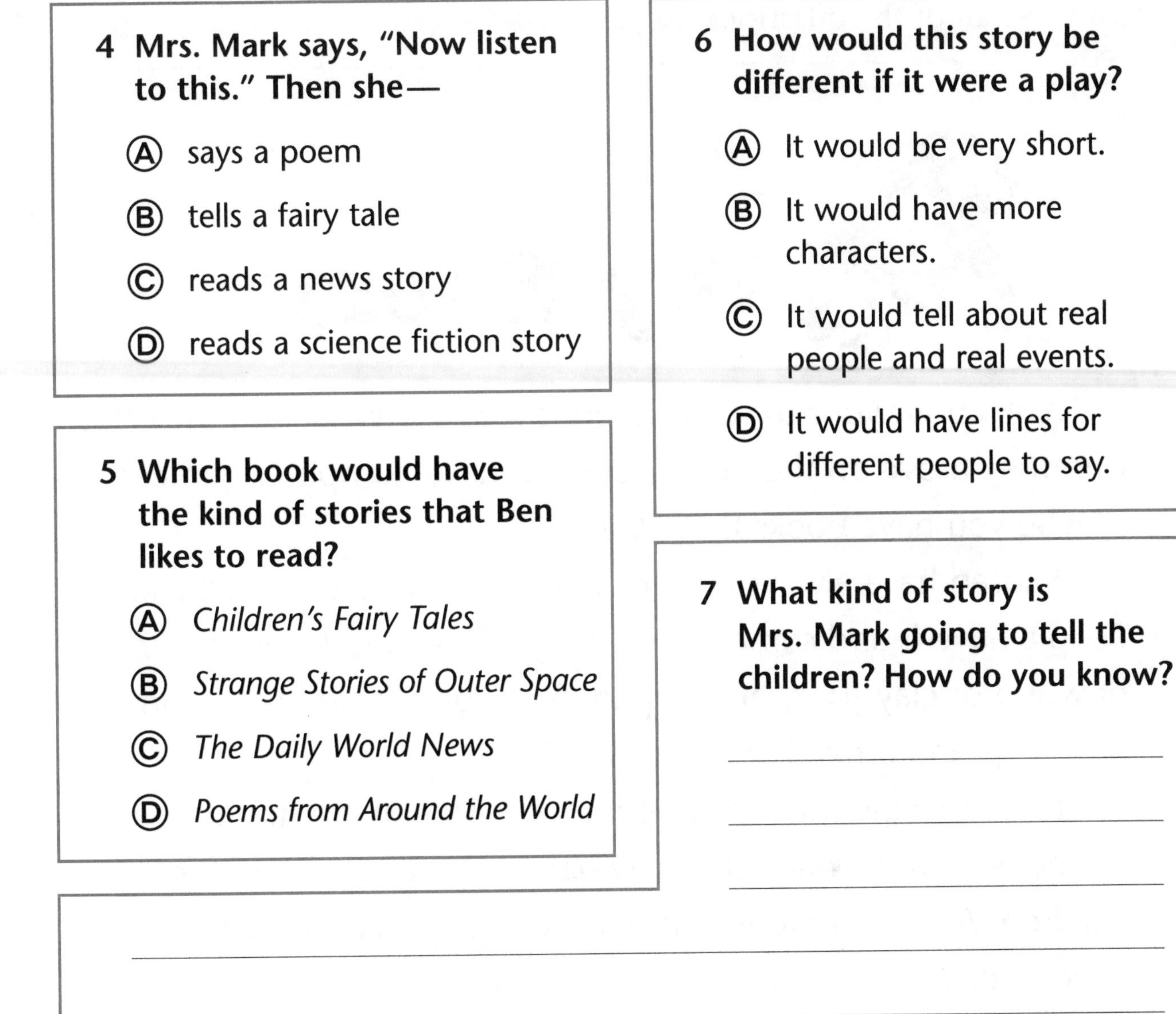

4 Mrs. Mark says, "Now listen to this." Then she—

Ⓐ says a poem

Ⓑ tells a fairy tale

Ⓒ reads a news story

Ⓓ reads a science fiction story

5 Which book would have the kind of stories that Ben likes to read?

Ⓐ *Children's Fairy Tales*

Ⓑ *Strange Stories of Outer Space*

Ⓒ *The Daily World News*

Ⓓ *Poems from Around the World*

6 How would this story be different if it were a play?

Ⓐ It would be very short.

Ⓑ It would have more characters.

Ⓒ It would tell about real people and real events.

Ⓓ It would have lines for different people to say.

7 What kind of story is Mrs. Mark going to tell the children? How do you know?

Skill 14: Prior Knowledge

This is information that you know before you read the passage.

Directions: Read the passage below. The passage is followed by questions that can be answered by using what you already know. Use this passage to answer all of the questions on pages 72–74.

Toy Story

1 Think about your toys. What are they like? What can they do? Can they move on their own? Do you have computer games? Maybe you have books that "talk."

2 Children have always had toys. But toys have changed a lot. People have found some very old toys. The oldest ones are made of wood or clay. They are shaped like people or animals. Some have legs and arms that could bend.

3 At first, people made their own toys. They made them one at a time. And they made them by hand. These toys were for their children. A mother would make a cloth doll. A father would carve a wood car.

4 Then some people began to sell the toys they made. The toys cost a lot because they took time to make. Some toys were made of heavy metal. That kind also cost a lot. So most children had just a few toys. Later, people found ways to make toys that cost less. They used machines. The machines could make many toys at once. They used tin. Tin was cheaper than heavy metal. Now more children could have more toys.

5 A big change came about fifty years ago. Toy makers began to use plastic. Plastic did not cost so much. Machines could make many plastic toys. And they could make them very quickly.

6 Also, toys could now move on their own. They lit up! They talked! Then came computers. Computers changed toys even more.

7 Some toys have not changed. The top is very old toy. It is still the same shape that it was long ago. It still spins. And kids still love it!

8 Pull toys are very old, too. They have wheels. They have a string so you can pull them around. Stores still sell pull toys. You might have had one when you were little.

9 The kite might be the oldest toy of all. Early paper kites could break easily. Now some are made of plastic. They can last longer than paper kites.

10 Toys have changed a lot over the years. And there are so many kinds of toys! What if you had only one toy? Which one would it be?

Modeled Instruction

Directions: Below is an example of a question that can be answered by using what you already know. Use the strategy help choose the correct answer.

1 Why are some kites made of plastic rather than paper?

Ⓐ Plastic kites only cost a penny.

Ⓑ Plastic comes in more colors.

Ⓒ Plastic will not break as easily.

Ⓓ Plastic is lighter than paper.

Strategy: Think about what you already know. Look for information in the passage that will help answer the question. Then choose the answer that makes the most sense to you.

Use this strategy to decide which answer is correct.

Ⓐ Plastic kites only cost a penny.

You already know that toys cost more than a penny. A plastic kite would cost more than that, too. Therefore, *choice "A" cannot be the answer.*

Ⓑ Plastic comes in more colors.

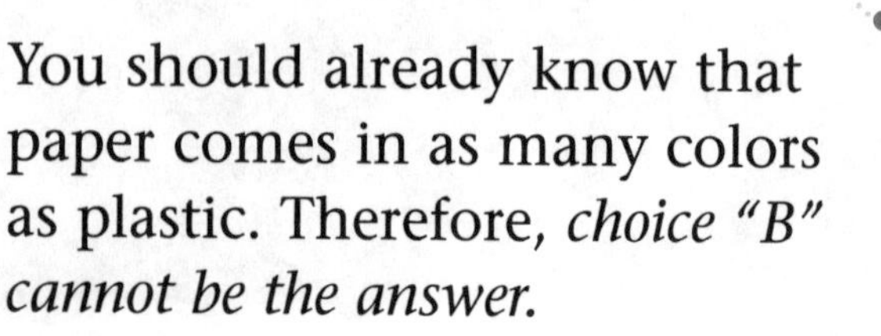

You should already know that paper comes in as many colors as plastic. Therefore, *choice "B" cannot be the answer.*

Ⓒ Plastic will not break as easily.

You already know that plastic is strong. The passage tells you that plastic kites can last longer than paper kites. This tells you that plastic will not break as easily as paper. So *choice "C" is the best possible answer.*

think!

Ⓓ Plastic is lighter than paper.

You have held paper. And you have held plastic. You already know that plastic is not lighter than paper. Therefore, *choice "D" cannot be the answer.*

Guided Instruction

Directions: Use the hints to answer the questions below. For question 2, you must choose the correct answer. For question 3, you will need to write out your answer.

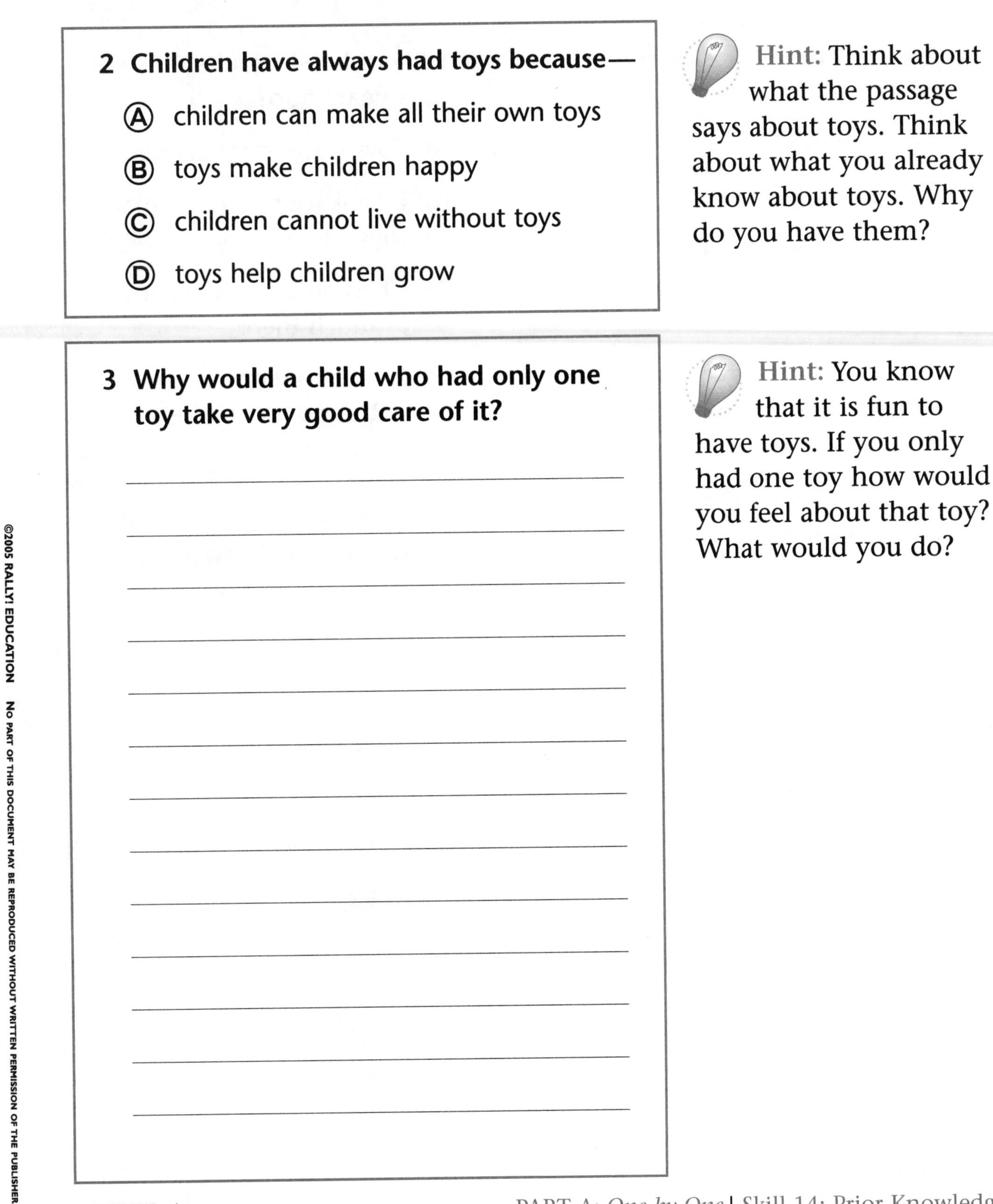

2 Children have always had toys because—

Ⓐ children can make all their own toys

Ⓑ toys make children happy

Ⓒ children cannot live without toys

Ⓓ toys help children grow

Hint: Think about what the passage says about toys. Think about what you already know about toys. Why do you have them?

3 Why would a child who had only one toy take very good care of it?

____

____

____

____

____

____

____

____

____

____

____

____

____

Hint: You know that it is fun to have toys. If you only had one toy how would you feel about that toy? What would you do?

Independent Study

Directions: Answer the following questions on your own. For questions 4, 5, and 6, choose the correct answer. For question 7, you must write out your answer.

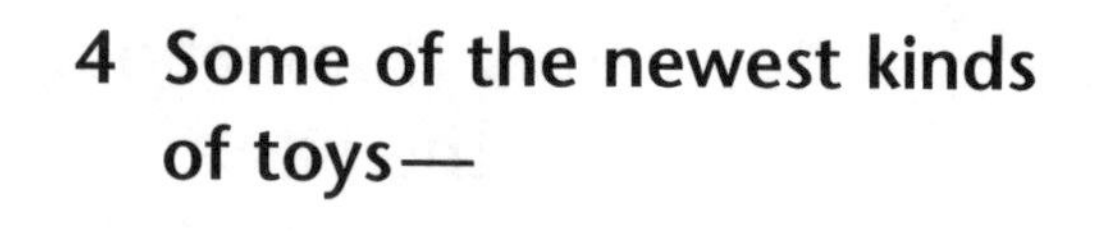

4 Some of the newest kinds of toys—

Ⓐ use paper

Ⓑ use computers

Ⓒ are made of cloth

Ⓓ are made of wood

5 Why do people still make pull toys?

Ⓐ Small children can play with them.

Ⓑ They are easy to make.

Ⓒ People can make a lot of money selling them.

Ⓓ Babies ask for them.

6 Why did children have fewer toys years ago?

Ⓐ Toys were more dangerous.

Ⓑ It took more time to make toys.

Ⓒ Children did not like toys as much then.

Ⓓ People thought toys were not good for children.

7 Name two of your toys. Tell what each toy is made of.

____

____

____

____

____

____

____

____

____

____

____

PART B

The 14 Essential Skills for Reading Success

All Together

Section 1: Modeled Instruction and Guided Instruction

Each of the fourteen reading comprehension skills are taught all together in this part. Part B is divided into two sections.

Section 1: Modeled Instruction and Guided Instruction

In this section, you will read a passage and answer fourteen questions. The questions will be both multiple-choice and open-ended. Each question covers one of the fourteen essential skills. There will be a *Reminder* to help you remember the strategy needed to answer each question.

Section 2: Independent Study

This section is made up of four different types of passages. All the passages are about one theme. Each passage has fourteen essential skill questions. You are on your own to answer them. At the end of the theme, there will be three questions about how the passages are connected to the theme.

Theme: *Up, Up, and Away*

B

Section 1: Modeled Instruction and Guided Instruction

On the pages that follow are several passages. Each passage is followed by fourteen questions. You will use the skills that you practiced in Part A to answer them. There are reminders below each question to help you remember which skill you should use to answer it.

Directions. Read the passage below. Then answer the questions that follow. Use the reminders to help you remember the strategy for answering each type of question.

A Surprise for Emma

1 Emma loved to go to the library. She went to the library almost every day. She had her own card.

2 She read books about farms. She read books about birds. Then Emma read a book about the sea. There were pictures of fish. There were red fish. And there were blue fish. There were pictures of starfish. There were pretty seashells.

3 Emma read more books about the sea. She told her mom and dad about the fish. She showed them the pictures. And she asked them many questions.

4 One day her mom said, "We will have a surprise for you on Saturday!"

5 Every day Emma asked, "What is the surprise?" But her parents only smiled.

6 "How many minutes until Saturday?" her dad asked Emma.

7 "Too many!" Emma said. They both laughed.

8 Then it was Saturday morning. Emma's stomach felt like it had butterflies in it! They drove into the city. They went into a big building. And there was the surprise. It was a very, very big fish tank.

9 There were so many fish in the tank! Emma saw fish that she had read about. She saw fish that were not in the books. Fish swam close to the glass! She could see how they moved. Emma thought it was all *wonderful.*

10 "I wish we had one of these at our house!" she said.

11 "Maybe we could start with something smaller," said her mom with a smile.

12 "This is the best surprise ever!" Emma said.

Directions: Answer the following questions using the reminders provided to help you recall the correct strategy for answering each type of question.

Facts and Details

1 Where did Emma get her book about the sea?

Ⓐ from school

Ⓑ from her friend

Ⓒ from the library

Ⓓ from her parents

Reminder: Look at the key words in the question. Find those words in the story. Read that part of the story. This will help you know what the answer is.

Main Idea

2 What would be another good title for this story?

Ⓐ "Emma and the Birthday Surprise"

Ⓑ "Emma and the Big Fish Tank"

Ⓒ "A Visit to the Library"

Ⓓ "Fish Are Funny"

Reminder: A good title tells you the main idea of a passage. Think about all the information you read. Decide what the main idea is. Ask yourself, "What is the passage **mostly** about?"

Sequence

3 What does Emma do after she takes out the book about the sea?

Ⓐ She asks a lot of questions

Ⓑ She reads a book about birds.

Ⓒ She gets her own library card.

Ⓓ She goes to the library for the first time.

Reminder: Find each answer choice in the story. Make a chart or timeline to show when each of these things happened. Be sure you put them in order. This will help you choose the correct answer.

Language and Vocabulary

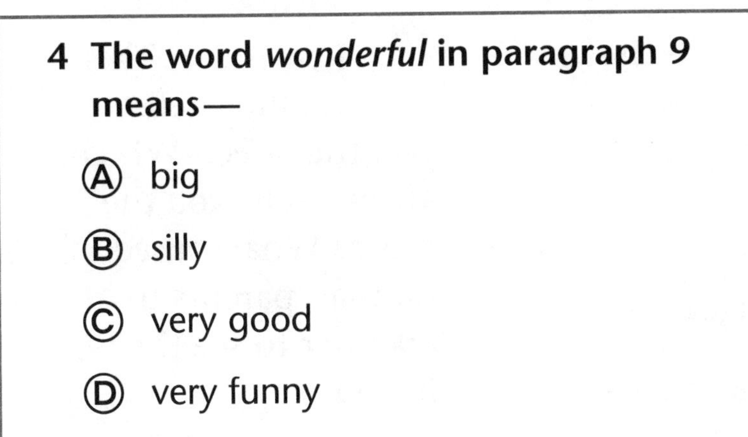

4 The word *wonderful* in paragraph 9 means—

Ⓐ big

Ⓑ silly

Ⓒ very good

Ⓓ very funny

Reminder: Think about how the word is used in the passage. This can help you to understand its meaning. Sometimes other words in the passage can also give you clues about the meaning of the word.

Character, Plot, and Setting

5 You can tell from reading the story that Emma's dad—

Ⓐ knows a lot about animals

Ⓑ does not like to drive

Ⓒ does not like the sea

Ⓓ likes to have fun

Reminder: This is a question about someone in the story. It is a character question. Think about Emma's dad. Think about what he does and says in the story. Choose the answer that **best** describes Emma's dad.

Cause and Effect

6 Emma's parents took her to see the big fish tank because—

Ⓐ they wanted to see it

Ⓑ they knew a lot about fish

Ⓒ they knew Emma would love it

Ⓓ they wanted Emma to read books

Reminder: This question tells you the effect. Which answer tells you the cause? What caused Emma's parents to take her to see the big fish tank?

Compare and Contrast

7 How is seeing the fish in the tank different from reading about them in the book?

Reminder: Compare means to tell how things are alike. Contrast means to tell how things are different. Use details from the story to support your answer.

Facts and Opinions

8 Which of the following is an opinion?

Ⓐ They drove into the city.

Ⓑ It was the best surprise ever.

Ⓒ They went into a big building.

Ⓓ Then Emma read a book about the sea.

Reminder: A fact is a statement that is true. An opinion is what someone believes is true. Which answers can be proven? Which answer cannot be proven?

Predict Outcomes

9 Which of the following will most likely happen soon?

Ⓐ Emma will get a small fish tank.

Ⓑ Emma will jump into the fish tank.

Ⓒ Emma will go to the city by herself.

Ⓓ Emma will not be interested in the sea.

Reminder: Find details in the passage that have something to do with the question. Decide what these details tell you. Figure out what will happen. This will help you choose the best answer.

Reach Conclusions

10 You can tell from reading this story that—

Ⓐ Emma likes to read

Ⓑ Emma lives by the sea

Ⓒ Emma likes to go to school

Ⓓ Emma goes to the city often

Reminder: Think about all the facts in the passage. The story does not tell you the answer. But it does give you the information you need to choose the correct answer.

Make Inferences

11 Why does Emma like to go to the library?

Ⓐ She has no place else to go.

Ⓑ She likes to talk to the librarian.

Ⓒ She can do her schoolwork there.

Ⓓ She learns many things from books.

Reminder: An inference is what is most likely to be true. Look at each answer choice. Find details in the passage about each answer. Decide which answer makes the most sense to you.

Point of View and Purpose

12 The author probably wrote this story so that—

Ⓐ people will like the sea

Ⓑ people can learn about fish

Ⓒ people can enjoy reading it

Ⓓ people will visit the fish tank

Reminder: Why the author wrote a passage is the purpose. Think about all the information in the passage. If you only think about just a few details, you may not understand why the author wrote this story.

Literary Forms and Sources of Information

13 This passage is an example of—

Ⓐ a news story

Ⓑ a story

Ⓒ a fairy tale

Ⓓ a poem

Reminder: There are many types of writing. Why would you read this passage? How is it written? Where would you find this story?

Prior Knowledge

14 If Emma wants to have her own fish tank at home, what will she have to buy?

Reminder: Think about what you already know. Also look for information in the passage that will help answer the question.

PART B

The 14 Essential Skills for Reading Success

All Together

Section 2: Independent Study

Theme

Up, Up and Away

Part B | Section 2: Independent Study

This section is made up of four different types of passages. All the passages are about one theme. Each passage has fourteen essential skill questions. You are on your own to answer them. At the end of the theme, there will be three questions about how the passages are connected to the theme.

Theme: *Up, Up, and Away*

Selection 1: *Hot Air Balloons* page 86
Selection 2: *To the Top* page 92
Selection 3: *Way, Way Up* page 98
Selection 4: *Our Sky* page 104

Section 2: Independent Study

There are four passages in this Section. All the passages have something to do with Up, Up and Away.

Theme: Up, Up and Away

Selection 1 | **Directions:** Read the passage below and answer the questions that follow.

HOT AIR BALLOONS

1 People love to fly. One way to fly is in an airplane. Another way to fly is in a hot air balloon.

2 Many people help fly a hot air balloon. There is a pilot. There are the people who ride in the balloon. And there are people who stay on the ground. They are called the ground crew.

3 Everyone helps set up the balloon. First, they lay the balloon on the ground. They put the basket next to the balloon. There are burners on the top of the basket. A big fan blows air into the balloon. Then the burners heat the air. The balloon fills with hot air. Warm air makes the balloon rise.

4 Ropes hold the balloon and the basket down. The riders climb into the basket. The pilot turns up the flame on the burners. The air in the balloon gets warmer. The people on the ground untie the ropes. The balloon rises into the sky. It is a very exciting ride.

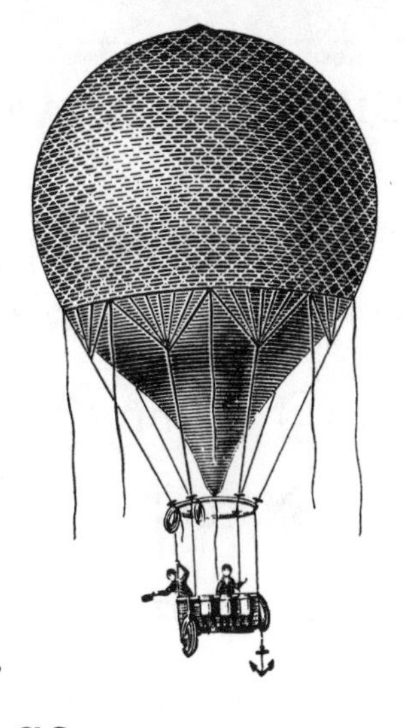

5 Now it is time to land. The pilot turns off the burners. The air in the balloon cools off. The balloon begins to sink down. It lands on the ground.

6 Balloons are a fun way to fly. You are in the open. You can feel the wind. You can see far away. It is very quiet. It is a *peaceful* way to travel.

7 There are problems with hot air balloons. They go the way the wind blows. Pilots do not know just where they will land. They have to look for a safe spot. Pilots watch the weather. The wind cannot be too strong. Landings can be bumpy. It takes a good pilot to land softly.

8 The wind is often calm in the morning. That is the best time for balloons to fly. So look for the beautiful balloons in the morning sky. Or take a ride yourself!

Directions: Answer the following questions on your own.

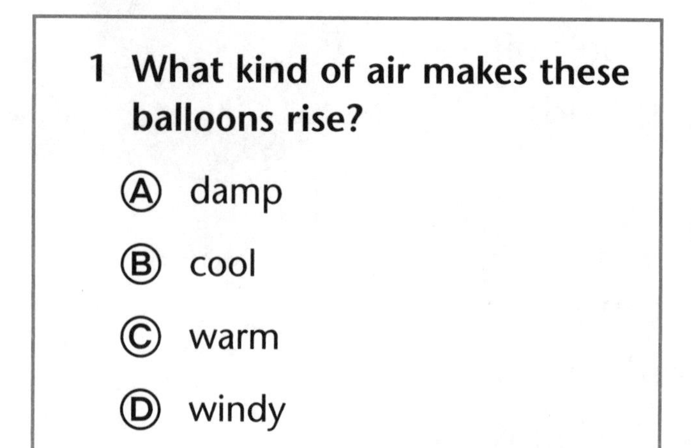

1 What kind of air makes these balloons rise?

Ⓐ damp

Ⓑ cool

Ⓒ warm

Ⓓ windy

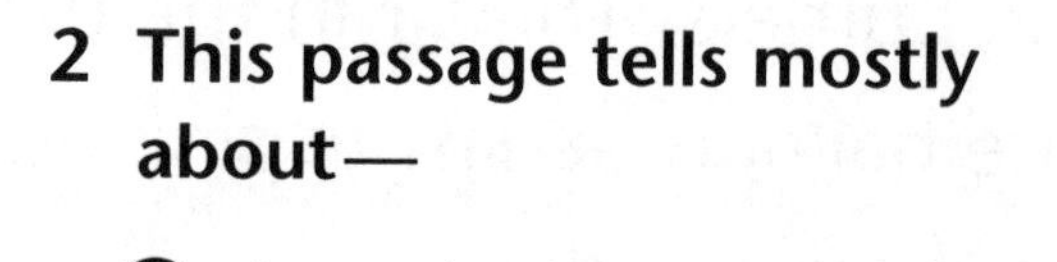

2 This passage tells mostly about—

Ⓐ how the burners work

Ⓑ how hot air balloons fly

Ⓒ how air gets into balloons

Ⓓ how hot air balloons land

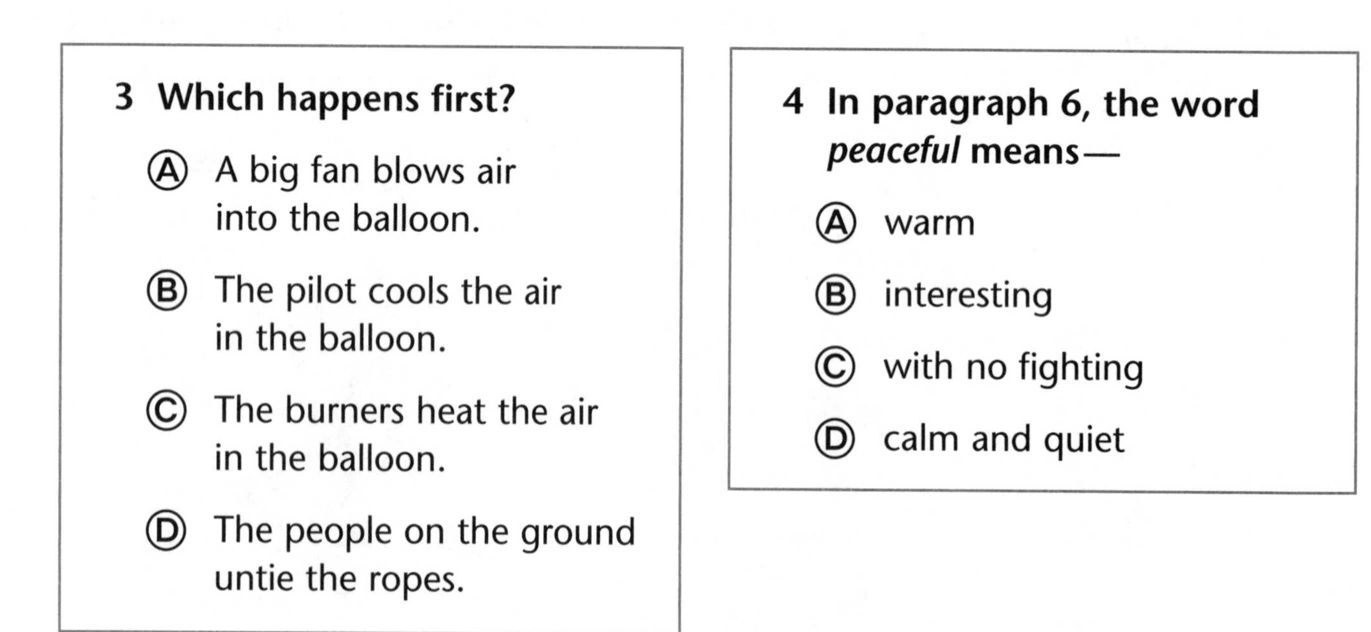

3 Which happens first?

Ⓐ A big fan blows air into the balloon.

Ⓑ The pilot cools the air in the balloon.

Ⓒ The burners heat the air in the balloon.

Ⓓ The people on the ground untie the ropes.

4 In paragraph 6, the word *peaceful* means—

Ⓐ warm

Ⓑ interesting

Ⓒ with no fighting

Ⓓ calm and quiet

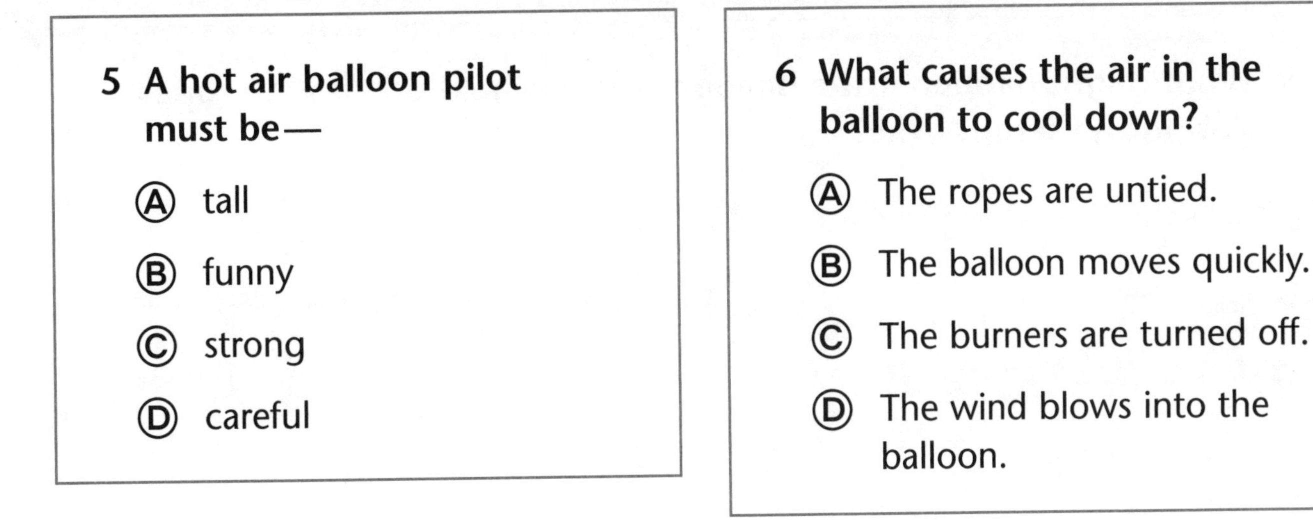

5 A hot air balloon pilot must be—

Ⓐ tall

Ⓑ funny

Ⓒ strong

Ⓓ careful

6 What causes the air in the balloon to cool down?

Ⓐ The ropes are untied.

Ⓑ The balloon moves quickly.

Ⓒ The burners are turned off.

Ⓓ The wind blows into the balloon.

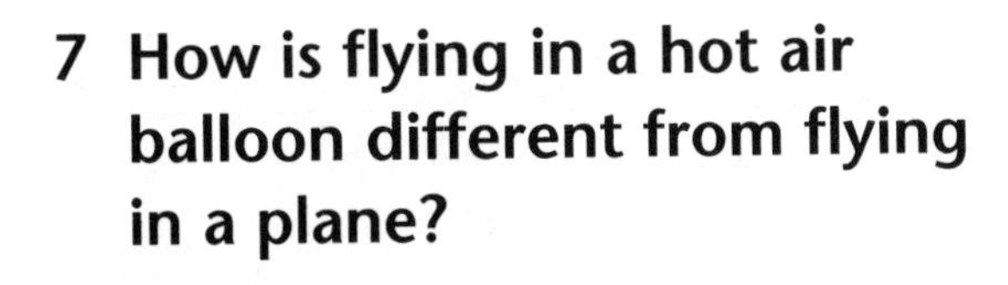

7 How is flying in a hot air balloon different from flying in a plane?

Ⓐ There is a pilot.

Ⓑ There are no walls.

Ⓒ The balloon takes you up into the air.

Ⓓ The balloon takes you from one place to another.

8 Which statement from the passage is an example of an opinion?

Ⓐ Balloons are a fun way to fly.

Ⓑ Warm air makes the balloon rise.

Ⓒ They go the way the wind blows.

Ⓓ The wind is often calm in the morning.

9 **What might happen if the balloon was not held down with ropes during the setup? Why?**

10 **A hot air balloon is the best way to travel—**

Ⓐ if you need to get somewhere quickly

Ⓑ if you need to get to a certain place

Ⓒ if many people want to fly together

Ⓓ if you want to fly for fun

11 **How can you tell from the passage that the author enjoys rides in a hot air balloon?**

Ⓐ The author is a balloon pilot.

Ⓑ The author knows a lot about flying.

Ⓒ The author talks about how much fun it is.

Ⓓ The author says the landing can be bumpy.

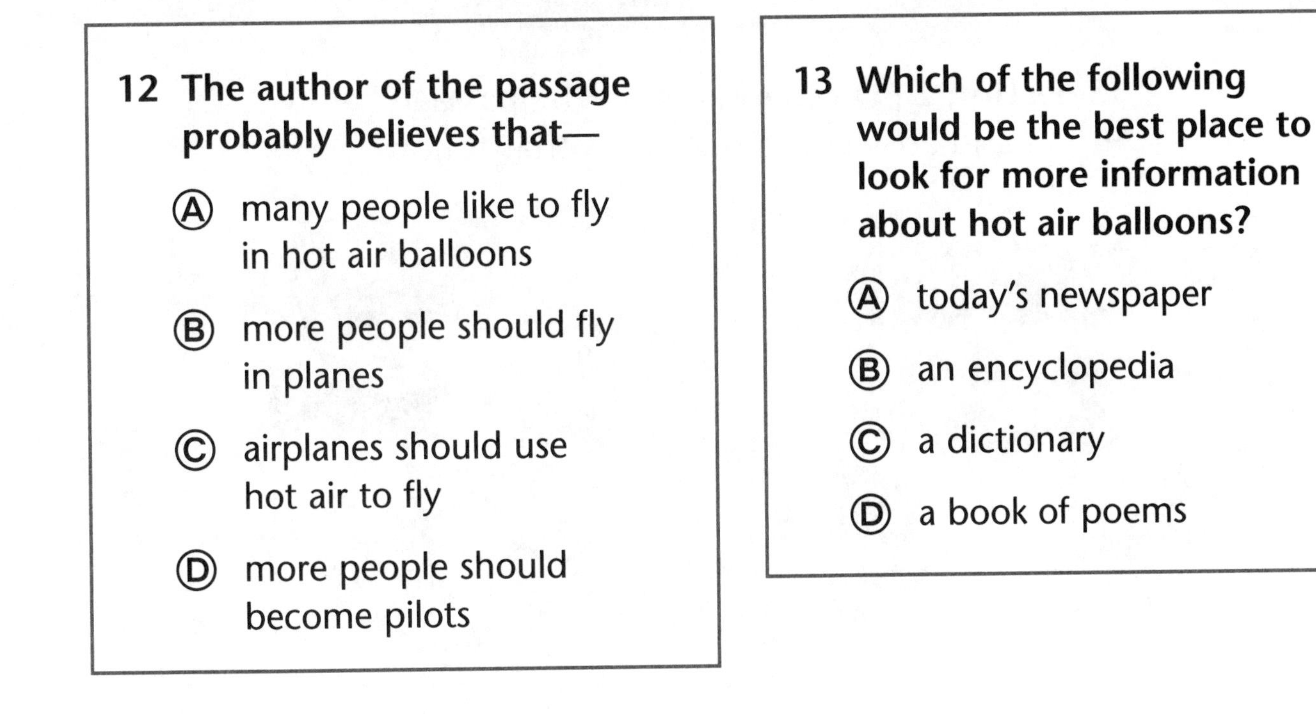

12 The author of the passage probably believes that—

Ⓐ many people like to fly in hot air balloons

Ⓑ more people should fly in planes

Ⓒ airplanes should use hot air to fly

Ⓓ more people should become pilots

13 Which of the following would be the best place to look for more information about hot air balloons?

Ⓐ today's newspaper

Ⓑ an encyclopedia

Ⓒ a dictionary

Ⓓ a book of poems

14 Would a hot air balloon or a plane be better for a long trip? Explain why.

____

____

____

____

____

____

____

____

____

____

Selection 2 | **Directions:** Read the passage below and answer the questions that follow.

1 Jenny answered the phone. "Hello?"

2 "Hey, Jenny! How is my favorite girl?" said her Uncle John. "And is my other favorite girl home?" he asked.

3 "Yes, I'm here," said her sister Amy. "I'm on the other phone"

4 "I have a plan," he said. "Let's go on a hike at Pleasant Mountain. I'll pick you up Saturday morning."

5 Both girls were excited. But Amy did not know if she liked to hike. Jenny thought it might be a lot of work.

6 Uncle John had made a list for them. He told them what to bring. The girls packed their backpacks on Friday night.

7 "This is a lot of stuff for a hike," said Amy.

8 "Uncle John said we must be *prepared,*" said Jenny.

9 On Saturday morning, the girls and their uncle drove to the mountain. They found the trail.

10 "Here we go!" said Uncle John.

11 They hiked for about an hour. The view was wonderful. They stopped for a snack.

12 Amy took off her warm shirt and drank some water. "We won't need our raincoats today," she said.

13 "You never know," said Uncle John. "There can be sudden storms up here. It is good to be *prepared!*"

14 Later, they reached the top of the mountain. A cool wind was blowing. They put their warm shirts back on.

15 "What is that over there?" asked Amy. "It looks beautiful."

16 "That is Mount Snow," said Uncle John. "It is higher than Pleasant Mountain."

17 "Let's climb it!" said Amy and Jenny.

18 "Mount Snow is very high, so it can have bad weather," answered their uncle. "I'll give you a very long list for that hike!"

Directions: Answer the following questions on your own.

1 Jenny and Amy are—

Ⓐ aunts

Ⓑ parents

Ⓒ friends

Ⓓ sisters

2 This passage is mostly about—

Ⓐ how to pack a bag

Ⓑ a hiking trip

Ⓒ how to find a trail

Ⓓ Uncle John

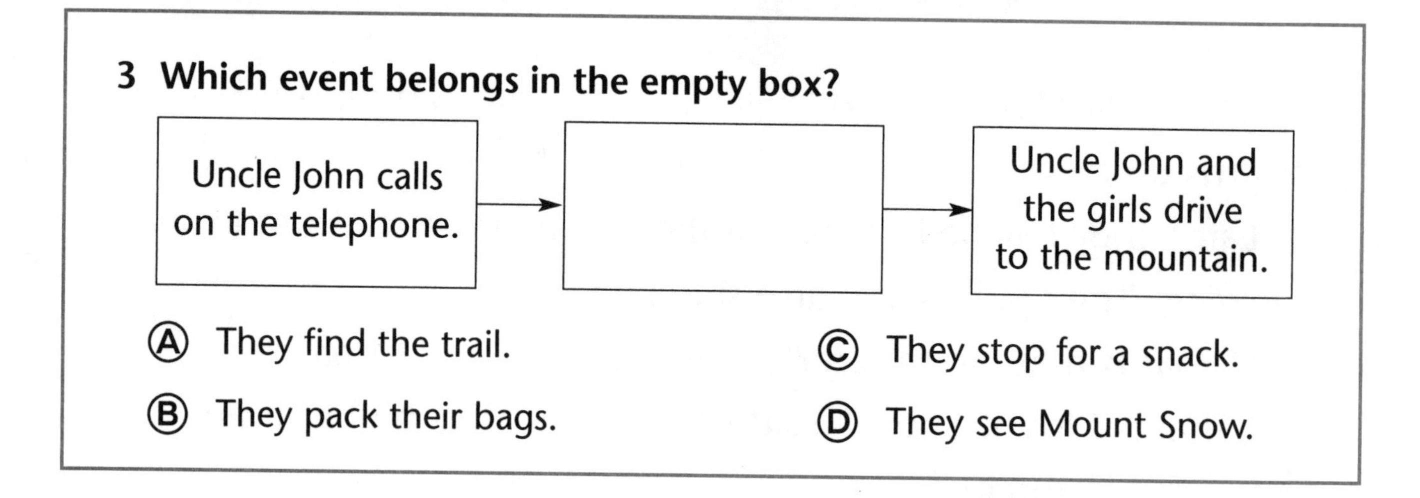

3 Which event belongs in the empty box?

Ⓐ They find the trail.

Ⓑ They pack their bags.

Ⓒ They stop for a snack.

Ⓓ They see Mount Snow.

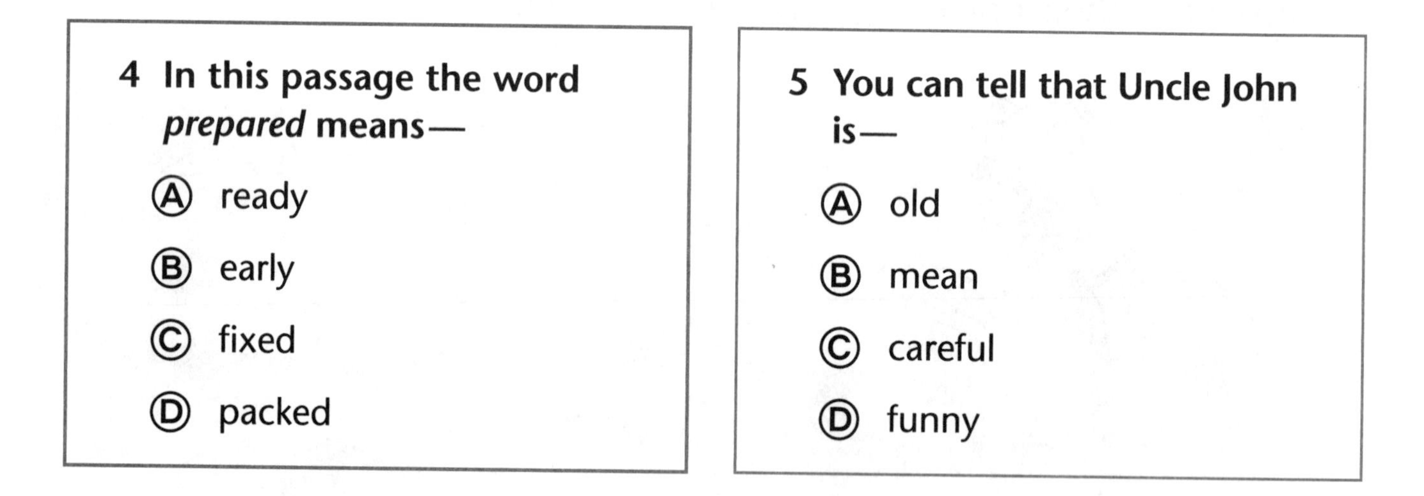

4 In this passage the word *prepared* means—

Ⓐ ready

Ⓑ early

Ⓒ fixed

Ⓓ packed

5 You can tell that Uncle John is—

Ⓐ old

Ⓑ mean

Ⓒ careful

Ⓓ funny

6 Why do the girls pack a lot in their backpacks?

Ⓐ They want to bring all their toys.

Ⓑ They want the packs to be heavy.

Ⓒ They know what they will need to have.

Ⓓ They pack what their uncle told them to.

7 **How are Pleasant Mountain and Mount Snow alike? How are the two mountains different?**

8 Which statement about Mount Snow is an opinion?

Ⓐ It looked beautiful.

Ⓑ It is higher than Pleasant Mountain.

Ⓒ A cool wind was blowing.

Ⓓ Mount Snow can have very bad weather.

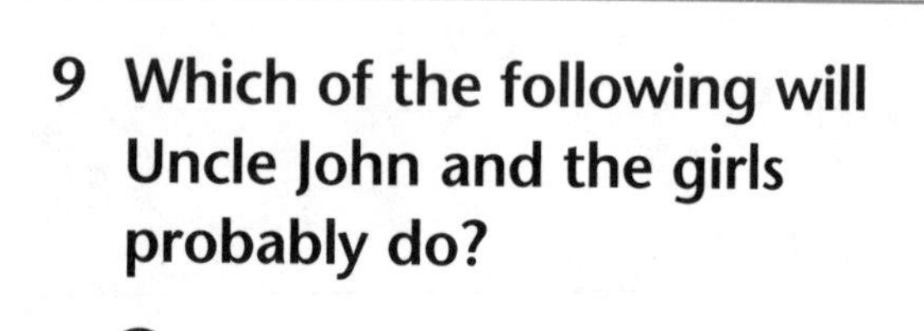

9 Which of the following will Uncle John and the girls probably do?

Ⓐ They will climb Mount Snow the next day.

Ⓑ They will hike on Pleasant Mountain again.

Ⓒ They will stop going on hikes.

Ⓓ They will hike every day.

10 Why did Amy take off her warm shirt?

Ⓐ The air was cool.

Ⓑ She did not like the shirt.

Ⓒ She felt hot with it on.

Ⓓ Jenny needed the shirt.

11 **Why do hikers need to bring raincoats on a nice day?**

12 **Why did the author probably write this passage?**

Ⓐ to teach a lesson

Ⓑ to tell people how to hike

Ⓒ to entertain

Ⓓ to tell about Mount Snow

13 **This passage is an example of—**

Ⓐ a play

Ⓑ a story

Ⓒ a fairy tale

Ⓓ a biography

14 **What will the hikers probably have to take with them when they climb Mt. Snow?**

Ⓐ less food

Ⓑ more water

Ⓒ more people

Ⓓ lighter clothing

Selection 3 | **Directions:** Read the passage below and answer the questions that follow.

Way, Way Up

by Pat Pryor

1 Way, way up in the bright blue sky
2 My new red kite
3 Went up so high.
4 Oh, I wish I could be there, too, I said.

5 Way, way up in the tallest tree
6 A red bird
7 Looked down at me.
8 Oh, I wish I could fly like you, said I.

9 Way, way up with the floating clouds
10 A silver plane
11 Flew over the crowds.
12 Oh, I wish I could be as high as you, I said.

13 Way, way up in the clear night sky
14 A bright star
15 Shone on high.
16 Oh, I wish I could twinkle, too, said I.

17 Way, way up with the twinkling stars
18 The pale moon
19 Gleams near Mars.
20 Oh, I wish I could watch some more, I said.

21 But now it's time to go to bed.
22 Good night, said I.

Directions: Answer the following questions on your own.

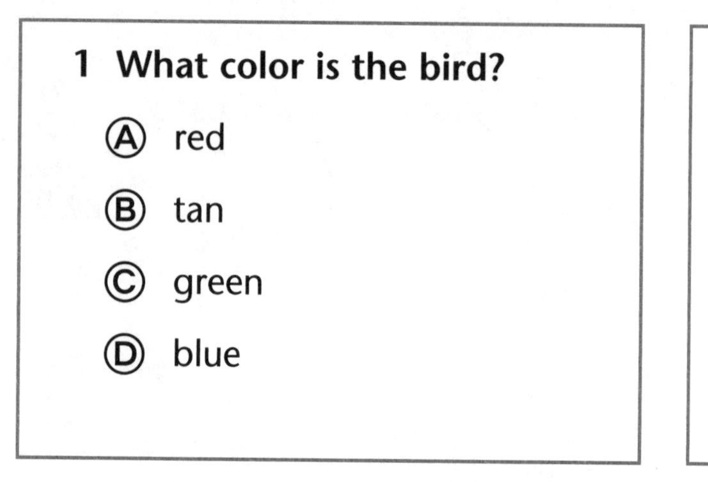

1 What color is the bird?

Ⓐ red

Ⓑ tan

Ⓒ green

Ⓓ blue

2 Another good name for this poem would be—

Ⓐ "Bedtime"

Ⓑ "Far Above Me"

Ⓒ "Nighttime"

Ⓓ "The Moon and Stars"

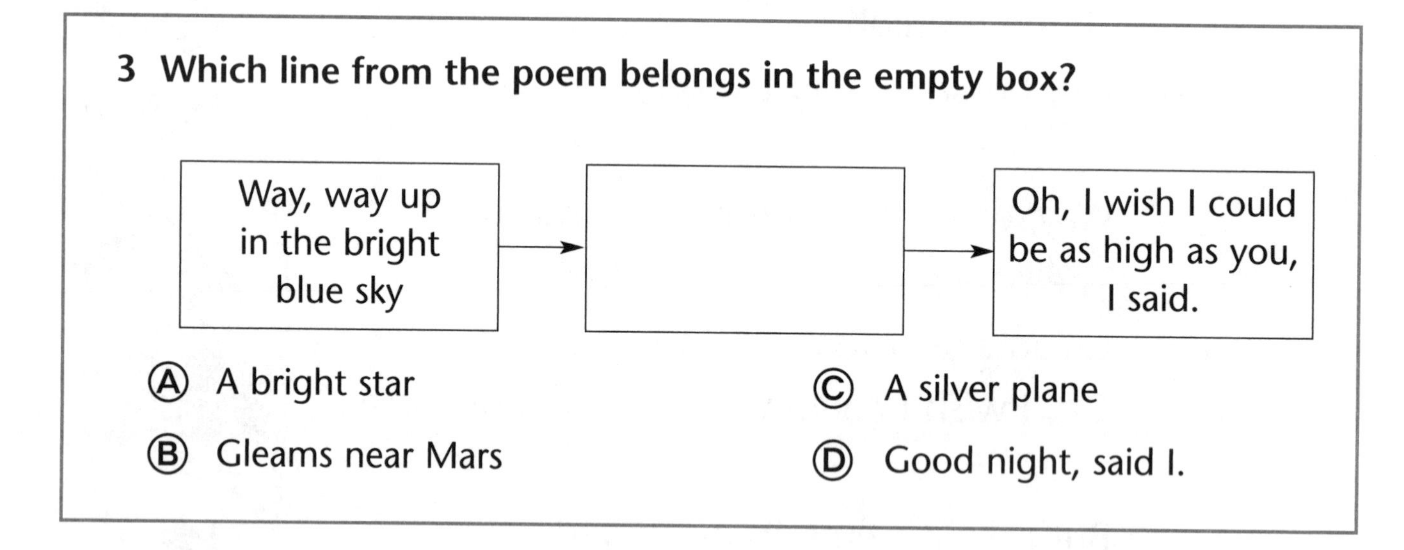

3 Which line from the poem belongs in the empty box?

Ⓐ A bright star

Ⓑ Gleams near Mars

Ⓒ A silver plane

Ⓓ Good night, said I.

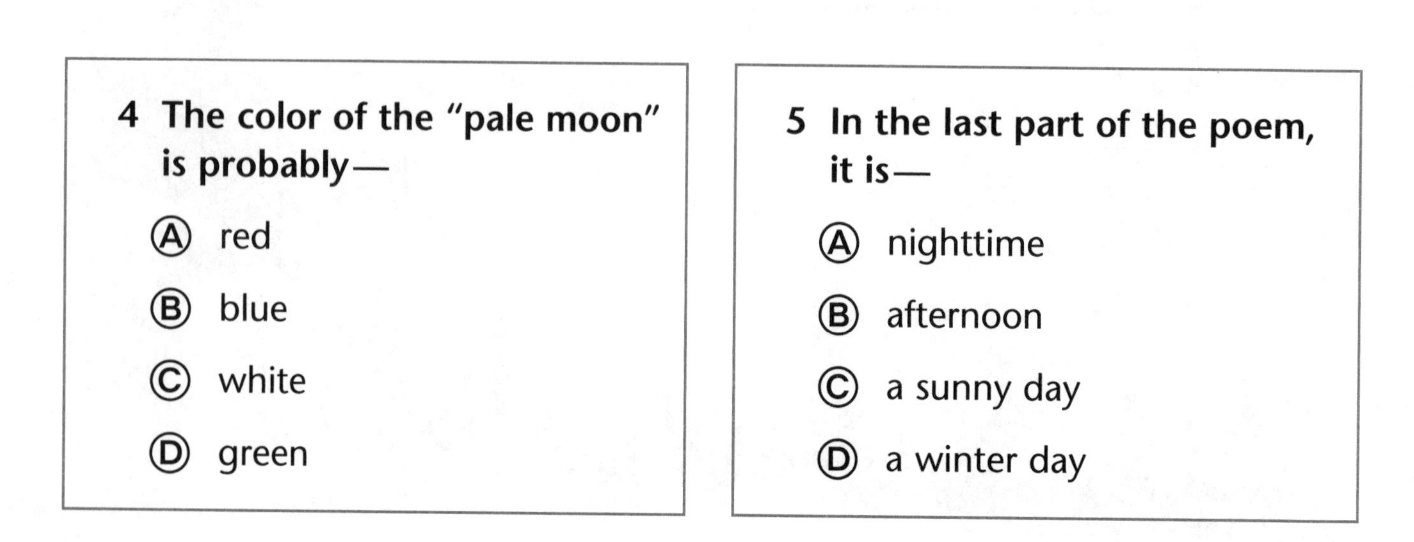

4 The color of the "pale moon" is probably—

Ⓐ red

Ⓑ blue

Ⓒ white

Ⓓ green

5 In the last part of the poem, it is—

Ⓐ nighttime

Ⓑ afternoon

Ⓒ a sunny day

Ⓓ a winter day

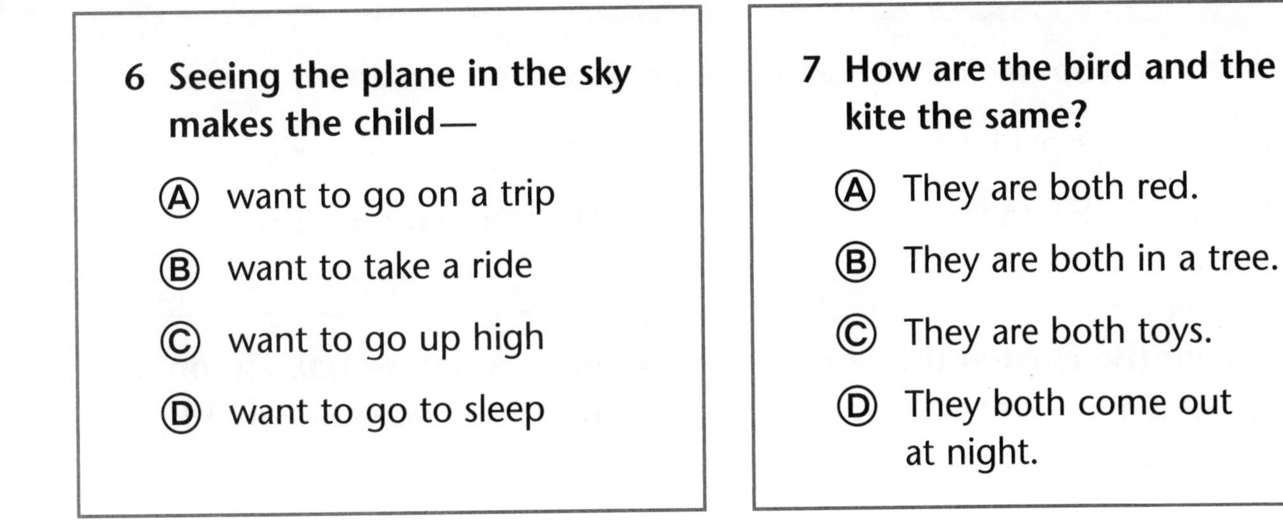

6 Seeing the plane in the sky makes the child—

Ⓐ want to go on a trip

Ⓑ want to take a ride

Ⓒ want to go up high

Ⓓ want to go to sleep

7 How are the bird and the kite the same?

Ⓐ They are both red.

Ⓑ They are both in a tree.

Ⓒ They are both toys.

Ⓓ They both come out at night.

8 Read the lines below from the poem.

A silver plane
Flew over the crowds.

Is this an example of a fact or an opinion? Explain your answer.

9 What do you think the child in the poem will dream about that night?

Ⓐ having a pet bird

Ⓑ being able to fly

Ⓒ buying a new kite

Ⓓ seeing more stars

10 Would the child in the poem want to ride in a hot air balloon or go down in a deep cave? Explain why you think the child would want to do that.

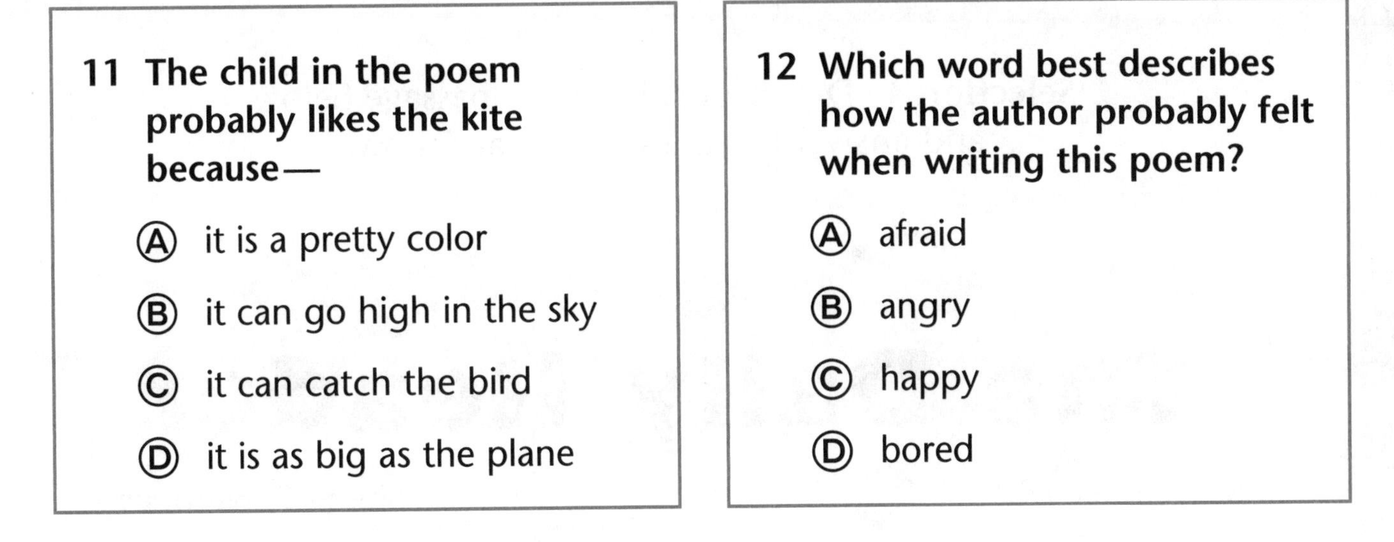

11 The child in the poem probably likes the kite because—

Ⓐ it is a pretty color

Ⓑ it can go high in the sky

Ⓒ it can catch the bird

Ⓓ it is as big as the plane

12 Which word best describes how the author probably felt when writing this poem?

Ⓐ afraid

Ⓑ angry

Ⓒ happy

Ⓓ bored

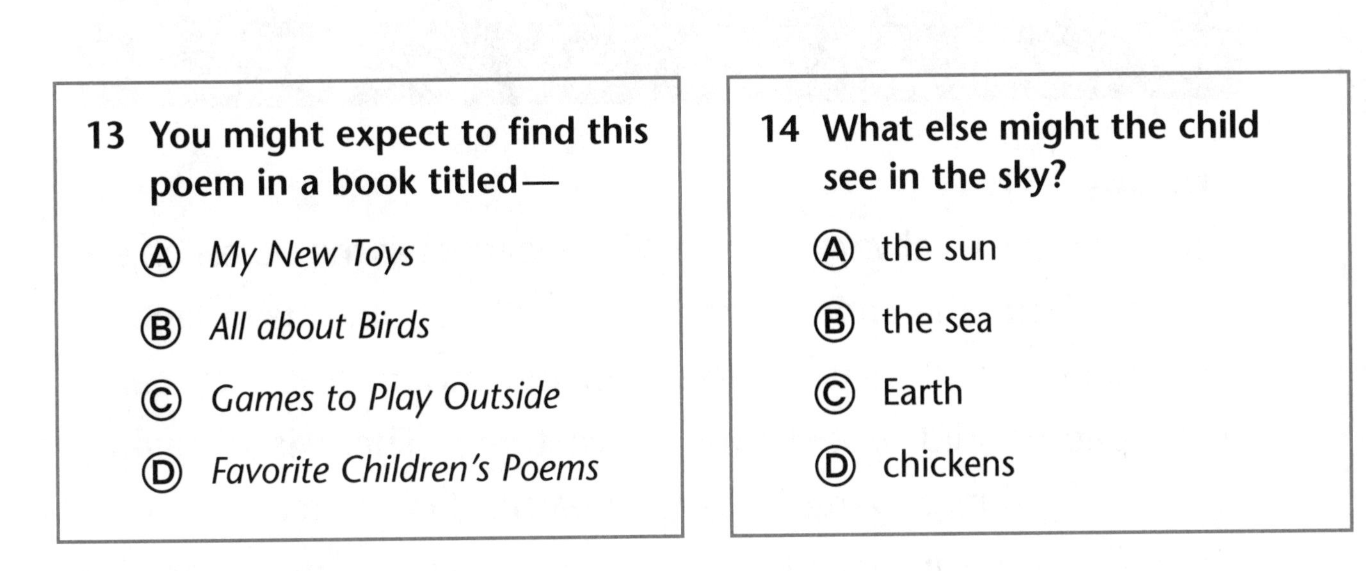

13 You might expect to find this poem in a book titled—

Ⓐ *My New Toys*

Ⓑ *All about Birds*

Ⓒ *Games to Play Outside*

Ⓓ *Favorite Children's Poems*

14 What else might the child see in the sky?

Ⓐ the sun

Ⓑ the sea

Ⓒ Earth

Ⓓ chickens

Selection 4 | **Directions:** Read the passage below and answer the questions that follow.

The Daily Reader

September 18th

Volume 9, Number 45

Our Sky

1 People have always been curious about the moon, the sun, planets, and stars. Years ago, people did not know what these things were. They knew that the sun gave them light. They knew that it made them warm. They knew that the stars would shine at night. But they did not know why.

2 We have learned more about the sky around us. But there is a lot we do not know.

3 The moon is the closest object to Earth. People have landed on the moon. But they can't live there. There is no air to breathe. Plants need air, too. So there are no plants on the moon. It is full of rocks. There are deep dents. The dents are called craters. And there are mountains on the moon.

4 The sun is the closest star to Earth. But it is much farther away than the moon. The sun

looks very big. But it is only a medium-size star. The sun is much too hot to explore. Mercury is the closest planet to the sun.

5 We need our sun to live. It gives us light. It makes us warm. It helps plants grow.

6 Venus is the closest planet to Earth. It is about the same size as Earth. It looks like a big star at night. Venus is very hot. It is too hot to explore.

7 Mars is a planet. It is about half the size of Earth. Some people think that we will visit Mars some day.

8 Our sky has many stars. Groups of stars make patterns in the sky. Long ago people named some of them. One pattern is called the Big Dipper. A dipper is a cup with a long handle. It is fun to learn what the patterns of stars look like. Then you can find them in the sky.

Directions: Answer the following questions on your own.

1 Which object in space have people been to?

Ⓐ Venus

Ⓑ the sun

Ⓒ Mars

Ⓓ the moon

2 This passage is mostly about—

Ⓐ stars

Ⓑ planets

Ⓒ star patterns

Ⓓ objects in the sky

3 Here are the the sun and the planets talked about in the passage.

Sun	Mercury	______	Earth	Mars

Which word should be on the empty line?

Ⓐ star

Ⓑ Venus

Ⓒ the moon

Ⓓ Big Dipper

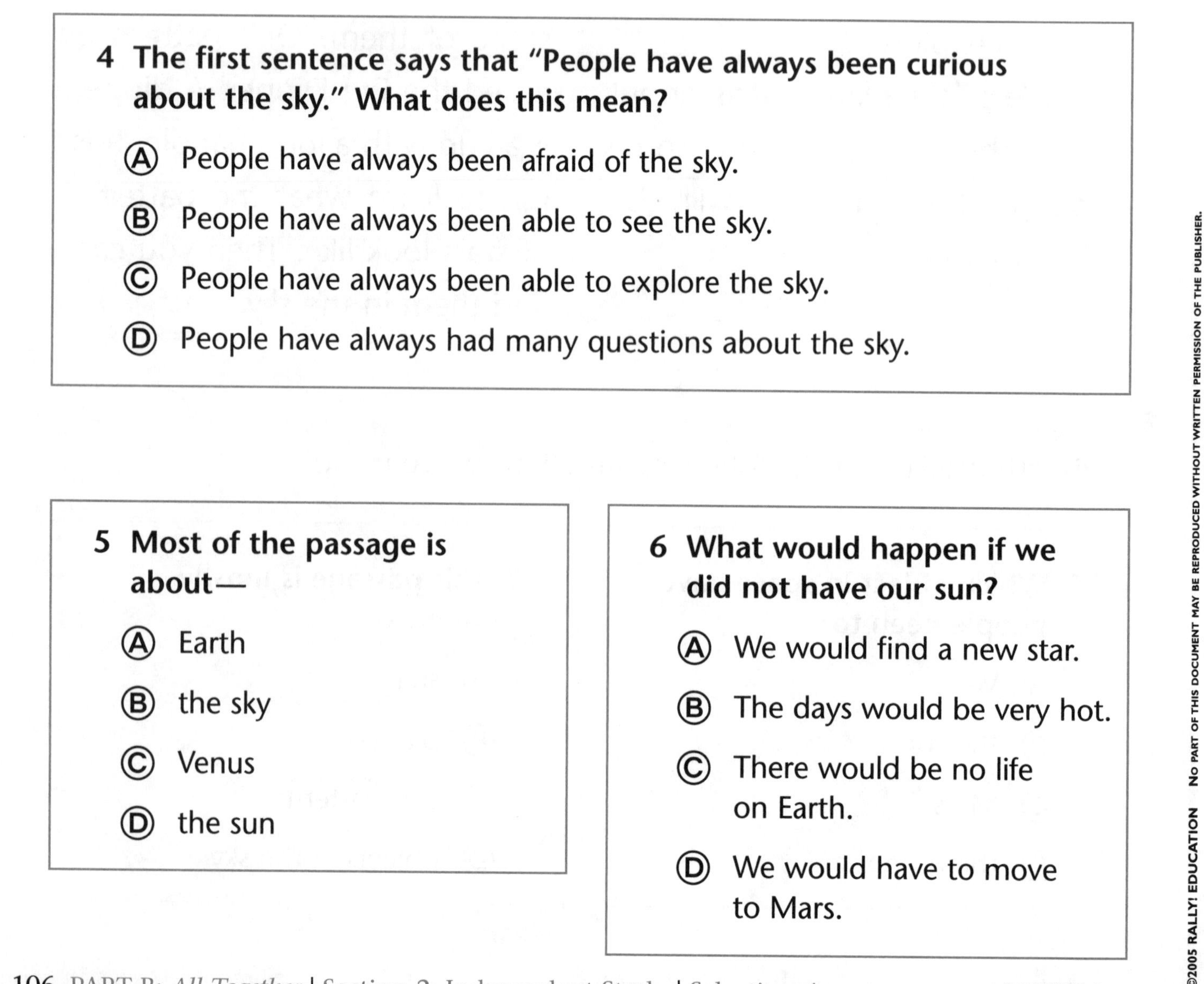

4 The first sentence says that "People have always been curious about the sky." What does this mean?

Ⓐ People have always been afraid of the sky.

Ⓑ People have always been able to see the sky.

Ⓒ People have always been able to explore the sky.

Ⓓ People have always had many questions about the sky.

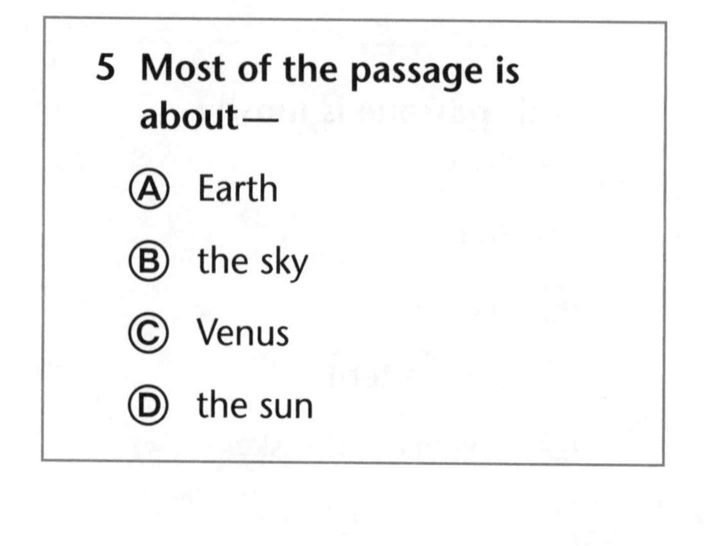

5 Most of the passage is about—

Ⓐ Earth

Ⓑ the sky

Ⓒ Venus

Ⓓ the sun

6 What would happen if we did not have our sun?

Ⓐ We would find a new star.

Ⓑ The days would be very hot.

Ⓒ There would be no life on Earth.

Ⓓ We would have to move to Mars.

7 Tell two ways Earth and the moon are alike. Tell two ways they are different.

8 Find a sentence in paragraph 8 that is an opinion. Tell why it is an opinion.

9 As the years go by, people will probably—

- Ⓐ try to live on the sun
- Ⓑ stop going into space
- Ⓒ not care about the sky
- Ⓓ learn more about the sky

10 The planets that are farther away from the sun—

- Ⓐ are colder
- Ⓑ are smaller
- Ⓒ have more craters
- Ⓓ have more life on them

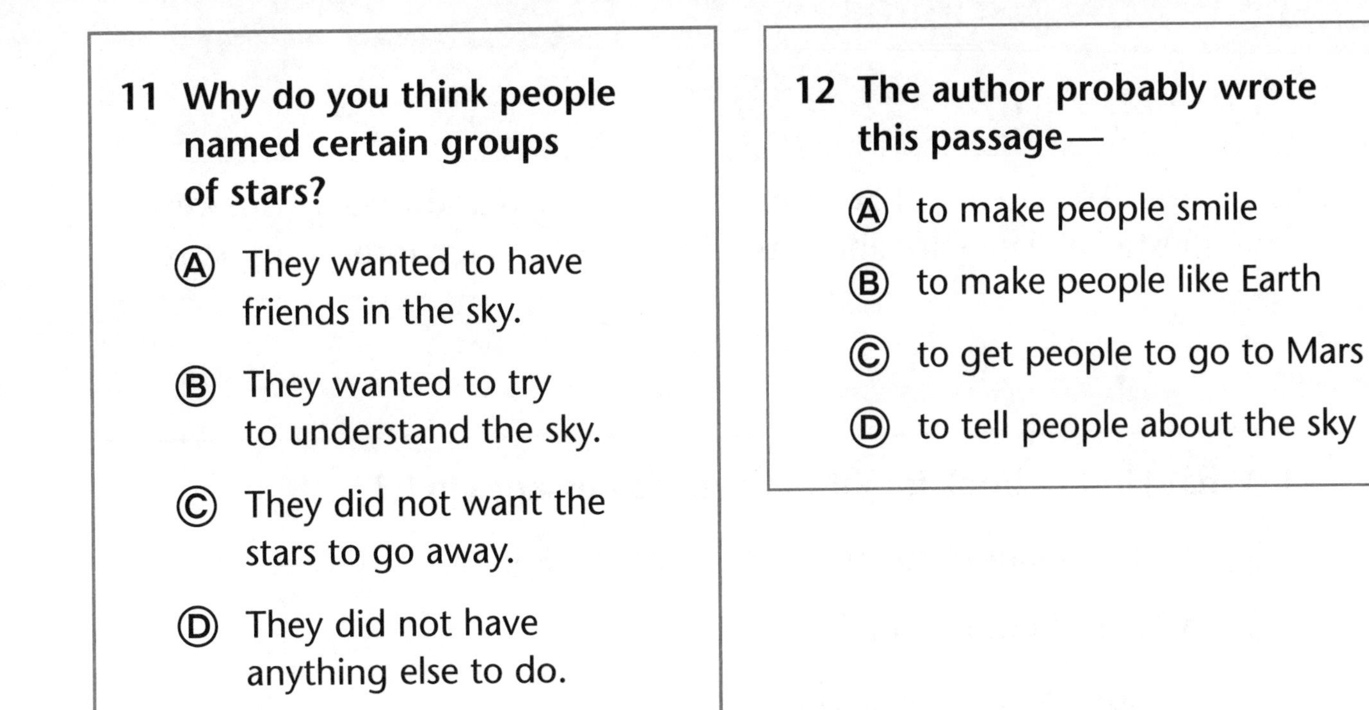

11 Why do you think people named certain groups of stars?

Ⓐ They wanted to have friends in the sky.

Ⓑ They wanted to try to understand the sky.

Ⓒ They did not want the stars to go away.

Ⓓ They did not have anything else to do.

12 The author probably wrote this passage—

Ⓐ to make people smile

Ⓑ to make people like Earth

Ⓒ to get people to go to Mars

Ⓓ to tell people about the sky

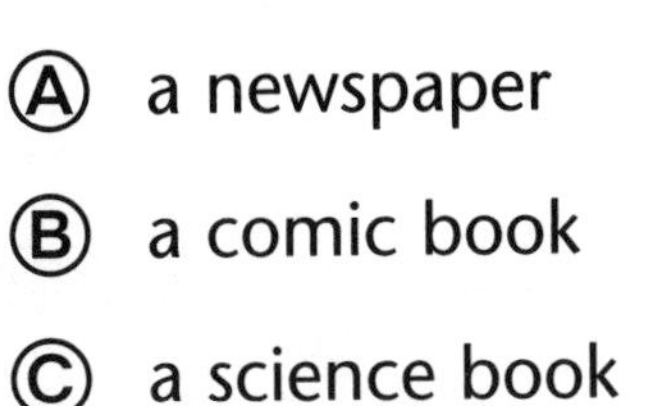

13 Where would you look to find more information about our sky?

Ⓐ a newspaper

Ⓑ a comic book

Ⓒ a science book

Ⓓ a story book

14 We should take good care of Earth because—

Ⓐ it is the only planet we can live on

Ⓑ it is the closest planet to the sun

Ⓒ it always has very nice weather

Ⓓ it does not have craters

Theme Questions

Directions: The theme of Section 2 was "Up, Up and Away." Answer these questions. They are about the four theme selections you just read.

1 What kind of book might have these passages in it?

Ⓐ a book about flying

Ⓑ a book about mountains

Ⓒ a book about life in space

Ⓓ a book about life on Earth

2 Tell how each passage has something to do with higher places.

3 What is the same about flying in a hot air balloon and climbing a mountain? What is different?

Notes